W9-BXC-280

If found, please contact:

_____

_____

Reward:

_____

The
FIVE MINUTE
JOURNAL

The simplest, most effective thing you
can do every day to be happier.

Intelligent
Change

intelligentchange.com

Intelligent Change

GET IN TOUCH
hello@intelligentchange.com

BE A STOCKIST
partner@intelligentchange.com

CREATED BY
Alex Ikonn & UJ Ramdas

DIRECTOR
Mimi Ikonn

Published by Intelligent Change.
Original edition ISBN 978-0-9918462-0-7
0080-07/2022

Printed in China on 100% recycled paper
certified by the FSC®

FSC
www.fsc.org

RECYCLED
Paper made from
recycled material

intelligentchange.com   **FSC® C074709**

To lifelong learners and doers.
You're changing the world
every day.

Those who don't believe in magic will *never find it.*

ROALD DAHL

The Five Minute Journal is not a magic pill.
Although, there is certainly some magic at work here.
You still have to do the work in the real world.

Get out of your comfort zone.
Take action and make magic happen.
This journal is your guide.

You are ready.

Contents

Five Reasons

You Will

Love

The Five Minute

Journal

1. IT'S THE SIMPLEST THING YOU CAN DO TO BE HAPPIER.

It's been proven over and over again that shifting your focus to the positive can dramatically improve your happiness. The key is consistency. With a positive quote every day, a weekly challenge, and a structure to help you focus on what's good, you will find The Five Minute Journal to be a great way to start and end the day.

2. IT'S BUILT ON PROVEN PSYCHOLOGY.

Somehow, it took psychologists about 80 years to realize that it's better to focus on positive behavioral traits as opposed to depression, anxiety, and disorders. This journal spares you the dense academic jargon behind this realization and incorporates it into practical routines you can implement simply and easily into your daily routine.

3. IT'S A JOURNAL FOR PEOPLE WHO DON'T WRITE JOURNALS.

If you are the kind of person who always wanted to write a journal, but life, excuses, and email took precedence, look no further. The Five Minute Journal was designed for you. Whatever your excuses are for not keeping a journal, this journal will eliminate them.

4. IT'S A SNAPSHOT OF YOUR POSITIVE EXPERIENCES.

Think of the feeling that arises when you smile nostalgically at an old photo of yourself. Imagine if you could have the same experience by just flipping to a certain day on a specific year in your life: you could zoom in on who you were, what you did, and how you felt on that day. It will be your own chronicle of memories, ideas, and dreams.

5. IT'S A COMMITMENT YOU CAN STICK TO.

Inside you will find ways to foolproof your commitment to writing frequently. How often do we shrink away from practices that we know are good for us? Unhealthy doctors, procrastinating professors, and unfaithful presidents prove this point. Simple and effective actions will get you in the habit of journaling every day and focusing on positive changes in your life.

We are what we
repeatedly do.
Excellence, then,
is not an act,
but a habit.

WILL DURANT

How it Works

Think of this journal as a toothbrush, but for your mind.

Every morning and night, we brush our teeth. It's a simple, quick, daily routine that happens almost without a thought. However, this seemingly effortless practice is crucially beneficial to our health. The Five Minute Journal works in precisely the same fashion—each page a cleansing bristle that dislodges negativity and leaves behind a healthier state of mind.

In today's world, we're frequently overwhelmed with stresses in our professional lives, disheartening stories in the news, and personal problems that wear us down. This journal harnesses the healing power of gratitude to help you refocus on the good. Consider it your mental insurance policy against negative thought loops, rejuvenating your mind and fortifying it against discontent.

Of course, when we heal and empower the mind our bodies return the favor. In a 2003 study by Emmons and McCullough, it was found that using a daily gratitude journal led to better sleep habits and reduced symptoms of physical pain.

While your toothbrush sits perched readily aside your bathroom sink, place this journal on your bedside table. Begin and end each day with a simple guided journey toward a more positive, refreshed, and grateful place. It just might improve your smile more than any triple-action whitening gel ever could.

So, let's get brushing.

The Five Minute Journal is the simplest, most effective thing you can do every day to become happier.

Basic Principles

Wisdom from ancient and modern times teaches us that the beginning and the end of the day are times to think, evaluate, and set the course. Regardless of when your day begins or ends, few people have established positive rituals that allow them to thrive.

Contrary to popular opinion, such established positive rituals are not restricted to the domain of ultra-successful entrepreneurs or Buddhist monks.

We recommend you keep this journal with a pen at your bedside. Let this be the first impulse when you wake up and the final impulse before you sleep. Let The Five Minute Journal hold that coveted spot on your bedside table, just an arm's reach away. You will be richly rewarded.

In about five minutes per day, you can establish a positive pattern of thinking and acting when it really matters. It's the ideal time window that allows for minimal effort and a life-changing reward.

Onward.

Early to bed, early to rise, makes a man healthy, wealthy *and wise.*

BENJAMIN FRANKLIN

WHY SHOULD I WRITE AS SOON AS I WAKE UP?

Have you ever had a day when you woke up and it felt like everything was going your way? Things felt easy, even effortless, and you couldn't help but smile? Is there a way that you can get a taste of that every day?

The Five Minute Journal is designed to help you do just that. You are fresh, still waking up and have the precious opportunity in the first few minutes to set the tone for the rest of the day. The journal asks you the precise questions that will create positive habit loops.

Make sure to write the journal first thing in the morning, even if you are:

Still sleepy? Thanks for sharing. Write it anyway.

Feeling unmotivated? Thanks for sharing. Write it anyway.

Late for work? Thanks for sharing. Write it anyway.

Growth isn't all roses and honey. It isn't always comfortable and it doesn't come with a cute bow tied over it. The reward of growth is priceless. Growth can lead to thriving life, fulfilling relationships, and improved well-being.

Resistance can get in the way of the growth you need. It causes depression, self-limiting beliefs, and, sometimes, credit card debt.

When you write the journal every morning, you push past resistance. You give yourself the opportunity to grow. You make the commitment to keep going, to make your mark on the world.

Never go to sleep without a request to your *subconscious*.

THOMAS EDISON

What do you typically do before you go to sleep? Do you have a routine?

The average American watches 5 hours and 11 minutes of TV per day.[1] If TV isn't as popular by the time you read this, then you are most likely on your phone or watching that Netflix show. Much of this happens just before sleep. What if you chose to use this time to invest in yourself? In your well-being?

Writing the journal before you go to sleep is a step in the right direction. Let it be one small positive habit that you do every day.

Spectacular results are a product of intelligent design and herculean consistency. Take the example of maintaining harmony in relationships. Some people's relationships have more drama than a reality TV show. Yet, there are others who continue to deepen their love and hardly fight.

There is a little known secret that is shared by couples in fulfilling relationships. It makes them happier and creates lasting bonds.

Here's the secret: They resolve any conflict before they go to sleep—with love, honesty, and trust.

In the same way, it is important that you write the journal before you go to sleep. You will find that The Five Minute Journal instantly helps you shift your focus on the positive and short-circuits negative thought loops. No matter how your day was, you will sleep a bit better than you would have otherwise. Simple.

Make sure to write the journal before going to sleep. Even if you:

Had a long day? Thanks for sharing. Write it anyway.

Have a pounding headache? Thanks for sharing. Write it anyway.

Have an early morning tomorrow? Thanks for sharing. Write it anyway.

The Morning Routine

Today's Gratitude List

One of the greatest strengths we possess as humans is our ability to focus our minds on whatever we choose. If you are perfectly calm and still on the inside, you can handle anything. For those of us without Zen training, the best way you can begin your day is by counting your blessings.

It is the antithesis of a bad-hair day or waking up on the wrong side of the bed. We suggest that whichever side of the bed you have put this journal, it is the right side.

No matter where you are and what your situation is, your focus can be shifted to something positive. Here is how it looks in practice:

I am grateful for...

1. *The warm bed that I sleep in.*
2. *My body that is working in perfect harmony with my mind.*
3. *The true and genuine friends in my life.*

OUR SECRET TO THE GRATITUDE LIST

Consider writing things you are grateful for that you may not yet have in your life. Let's say you really want to be in a healthy relationship. Then write... *I am grateful to be in a loving, healthy relationship with a partner of my dreams.* Just do not forget to clearly define this person, which is a whole different exercise.

What is Gratitude?

It is an emotion that defies easy classification. Gratitude, derived from the Latin word *gratia* (meaning grace, graciousness or gratefulness) eludes simple explanation by academics. Definitions such as "the willingness to recognize the unearned increments of value in one's experience" look great on term papers but don't get the point across. We will not attempt to disguise imprecision with ten-dollar words.

Gratitude is the experience of counting one's blessings.

It is the feeling that embodies the phrase "Thank you". It is the unexpected reward of a kind deed that is magically produced by your brain. It is the inexplicable feeling in your body that makes you smile at strangers.

Why do scientists love gratitude? Even after cutting through the smoke of Law of Attraction-style belief systems, gratitude has shown to be quite transformative in humans ranging from students to retirees.

A 2003 study by Emmons and McCullough found that keeping a daily gratitude journal leads to better sleep, reductions of physical pain, a greater sense of well-being, and a better ability to handle change.[2]

Delving deeper into the world of brain science, there's another study that illustrates the immediate effectiveness of gratitude. Turns out, gratitude could be the ultimate magic pill for "happiness" (drugs notwithstanding).

In a 2008 study, subjects experiencing gratitude were studied under fMRI (functional Magnetic Resonance Imaging) and it was found that they were influencing their hypothalamus in real-time.[3]

The hypothalamus is the small but powerful part of your brain that directly influences sleep, eating, and stress. Gratitude also stimulates the part of the brain associated with the neurotransmitter dopamine—the "do it again" chemical—that is responsible for the creation of new learning pathways.

Bottom line: writing in this journal each morning and night can help you gain a more positive outlook on life.

Creating
a Better Day

WHAT WOULD MAKE TODAY GREAT?

Have you ever had the experience of buying a new car and seeing the same model everywhere you go?

Or automatically noticing how someone has the same shoes/haircut/shirt? Have you had the experience of falling in love and seeing the world through rose-colored glasses?

These experiences are universal, but why do they happen?

There is a small part of your brain called the Reticular Activation System (RAS) that turns on and off your perception of ideas and thoughts and determines the lenses through which you look at the world. When you take an action like buying a new car, you have taken a major step in redefining your possessions and your RAS changes to accommodate your new acquisition. Everywhere you go, your RAS will gently remind you of this change by pointing out others who have the same car as you.

When you write "What would make today great?" you are taking a step to influence your RAS to point out and engage in activities that would make your day better. You are building new pathways in your brain that allow you to "see" what you can do to improve your well-being every day.

You are creating a new program in your mind that naturally increases your happiness. Doing this consistently gives you consistently better days. It is that simple.

One study found that people who simply thought about watching their favorite funny movie actually increased their endorphin levels (the chemical your brain produces to make you feel happiness and well-being) by 27 percent.[4] The most enjoyable part of an activity is often the anticipation.

To illustrate this with an example, let's introduce you to Katie. She is an ambitious twenty-something whose favorite part of The Five Minute Journal is "What would make today great?" because it gives her an excuse to brainstorm ideas to spice up her day. As soon as she wakes up, she spends an extra minute before writing out this section.

This is what a random day in her journal looks like:

What would make today great?

1. Taking extra time for myself before leaving for work.

2. Going for a walk after lunch.

3. Getting to sleep before 10 PM.

Notice she makes sure she writes down what she has control over.
She could write about being grateful for a sunny day; however, she has
no control over whether the day would be sunny or not. She focuses
on the specific actions she can take in the day to make it great.
So, it's your turn now. How could you make today great for you?

It's the *repetition of affirmations* that leads to belief. And once that belief becomes a deep conviction, things begin to happen.

MUHAMMAD ALI

Daily Affirmation

If you have read this far, chances are you are interested in creating something amazing in your life and you are going to achieve it. You have ideas about the person you want to be and the future you want to build.

Let's consider a study conducted by Dr. Alia Crum and Dr. Ellen Langer from Harvard University. They performed an experiment to study the effect of brain priming on the staff of seven different hotels. Half of the participants were informed about how much exercise they were getting every day through their work—how many calories they burned, how similar vacuuming is to a workout, etc. The other half were given no such information.

Several weeks later, it was found that the first group who had been primed to think of their work as exercise had actually lost weight. Incredibly, these individuals had not done any more work or exercised any more than the control group (their colleagues who had not been informed about how their work was similar to a workout).[5]

Hence the operative question—how can you prime your brain to cash in on this?

The Daily Affirmation is a simple statement that defines you as you want to be. Every time you write the daily affirmation, you prime your brain to start building this belief in your mind. With consistency, you will begin to create that change from within.

HERE IS HOW IT WORKS IN PRACTICE.

Let's say Bruce is interested in building his confidence in everyday life. He wakes up in the morning and writes in his journal:

Daily affirmation

I am confident and comfortable in my own skin.

As he goes about his day, he naturally starts to notice the world from this perspective. Let's say he buys some tea and smiles at the cashier. His subconscious begins to think, "Ah, this must be happening because I am confident and comfortable in my own skin." Every day he writes in The Five Minute Journal, he begins to prime his brain to this belief.

Don't underestimate the effectiveness of this exercise. If Will Smith, Jim Carrey, and Arnold Schwarzenegger found value in it, you can too.

HERE ARE SOME EXAMPLES OF HOW THIS LOOKS IN THE JOURNAL:

Daily affirmation

I am able to live with passion and purpose.

YOU COULD ALSO GET NICE AND SPECIFIC:

Daily affirmation

I am in a loving and passionate relationship.

Earning $100,000 per year.

The Night Routine

Highlights of the Day

Possibly the best moment in the day is allowing yourself to take inventory of special moments—big and small. Highlights of the Day is your personal collection of the expected and unexpected bounty of good things that you experienced in a day.

To illustrate the effectiveness of this one section, we turn to Quora—a social networking website that allows intelligent people around the world to share insights, answers, and knowledge. A question relating to happiness gleaned a powerful response from a social marketer, Brad Einarsen, which was supported by leading psychologists such as BJ Fogg.

❝

BRAD EINARSEN

When I was in a dark period, I instituted a simple rule that changed my life.

Rule:
When I arrive home from work, the very first thing I tell my wife is the best thing that happened that day.

No exceptions. No complaining. Just the best thing that day, even if it was just a good cup of coffee. This had the effect of starting our evening off on a positive note and it changed our relationship.

❞

THE HIGHLIGHTS OF THE DAY IN ACTION

To investigate the power of focussing on three good things every day, a group of ICU (Intensive Care Unit) staff were invited to participate in a 14-day study. During the study, the ICU personnel, a group who typically have a higher level of job-related burn-out and post-traumatic stress disorder, were asked to reflect on the questions: "What are the three things that went well today?" and "What was your role in bringing them about?". Researchers identified 3 main themes—having a good day at work; having supportive relationships; and making meaningful use of leisure time—and concluded that focusing on three good things each day not only promoted wellbeing, but also helped to strengthen resilience among the healthcare workers.

FOR THE FIRST FEW WEEKS OF LISTING YOUR HIGHLIGHTS OF THE DAY, START WITH SOMETHING SIMPLE:

Highlights of the Day

1. *A friend recommended a wonderful book for me.*

2. *I took a beautiful walk in the park today.*

3. *Barista remembered how I like my Americano.*

It can truly change your perspective and life outlook. When you write down highlights of the day, you count your blessings—in reverse. This has the effect of allowing you to "prime" your brain in reverse and can change not just your relationships with your loved ones, but your relationship with yourself.

Slowly, you will start to improve at this. Through the power of discipline, the list will start getting better and better. Remember to review Highlights of the Day every month to see how you are changing by focusing on the good in life.

Acknowledging Lessons of Every Day

BECOME BETTER BY DIVING INTO LESSONS LEARNED AND KNOWLEDGE GAINED FROM EVERY DAY.

Most of our days blend into one another, yet continuous and consistent reflection gives us an opportunity to find out that there is always something different, valuable, and insightful in every day. It also encourages us to think about how we can cultivate more intention, joy and meaning in our life.

Finding lessons from every day may be just one of the secrets to your success and emotional wellbeing, because acknowledging daily life lessons, challenges, and setbacks without letting them define who you are is a great act of courage, self-awareness, and mindfulness.

How it works: Review, evaluate and reflect on every aspect of your day. Take a look at your emotional state, at your work, and your relationships. What went right? What can be improved?

Helpful hint: Use your everyday experience as a valuable learning tool to become better, grow, and unleash your full potential. This is how the growth mindset is built.

It could be finding inspiration in the success of others.
It could be starting your day in control by waking up earlier.
It could be feeling more present when you turn off your phone.

This section is your daily reminder to take full responsibility of your life and shape your own reality. Letting go of what holds you back and turning it into valuable lesson sets you on the path for a more fulfilling tomorrow. It helps you navigate through the challenging times, recognise the good in every day, and live with the intention and purpose.

Let's say today Robin is feeling anxious and stressed because of a very busy schedule at work. She feels like spending some quality time with her loved ones may help her wind down and relax. She decides to log off from work at 7 PM. When she writes in this section, Robin realises she was able to feel calmer and more present at family dinner because she listened to herself, prioritised her wellbeing, and committed to finish her work on time.

SHE WRITES:

What did I learn today?

Always listen to your body - it knows when you need to rest.

And she begins to start building a pattern where she reflects on every day and discovers valuable lessons in her daily choices and actions. In time, this exercise can shift how you react to what every new day brings and help you use your experience as a powerful method for growth and positive change.

HERE ARE MORE EXAMPLES:

What did I learn today?

Reading before the workday starts puts me in a better mood.

Drinking mint tea in the evening helps me fall asleep faster.

**MOST PEOPLE FIND THEMSELVES SMILING WHEN
THEY ARE WRITING THIS (HINT, HINT).**

The ultimate measure of a man is not where he stands in moments of *comfort and convenience*, but where he stands at times of *challenge and controversy*.

MARTIN LUTHER KING, JR.

Weekly Challenges

Whatever your definition of growth may be, the only way to self-growth and development is through challenging yourself, your beliefs, and your abilities. Challenge brings improvement—and change leads to progress.

We often talk about what we want out of our life and sometimes it's where those conversations about dreams end—with us simply talking about it. Building your dream life requires you to step out of your comfort zone and actually make things happen. The more you challenge yourself and experience the positive emotions from fulfilling your goals, the greater is your confidence.

The weekly challenges we curated in this journal will encourage you to reflect on your values, enjoy simple pleasures of life, and take actions beyond your comfort zone, where real growth happens. Challenges are given on a random day of the week instead of the daily quote.

Treat each challenge as a mission and experiment in your life. You might just enjoy yourself in the process.

My
Commitment

I, _____ Chloe Moore _____,
commit to writing The Five Minute Journal for at least 5 days in a row,
starting _____ May 1 _____.

Writing this journal is really important to me because
I am committing to my best life.
I want to create more abundance in my life.
I need more discipline in my life.

If I finish 5 days of writing this journal, I will reward myself with
A ski trip with my significant other.

If I don't finish 5 days of writing this journal, I will promise to
Donate $100 to a charity I don't support.

I will do the following things to ensure that I do
The Five Minute Journal every day:
Keep my Five Minute Journal right by the bedside.
Brush my teeth only after I've done the journal.
Set my alarm only after I do my night journal.
Share my commitment with someone I love.
Sign up for tips at www.journalhabit.com.

FILL IN THE BLANKS

I, _____,
commit to writing The Five Minute Journal for at least 5 days in a row,
starting _____.

Writing this journal is really important to me because

_____

_____

_____

If I finish 5 days of writing this journal, I will reward myself with

_____

If I don't finish 5 days of writing this journal, I will promise to

_____

I will do the following things to ensure that I do
The Five Minute Journal every day:

_____

_____

_____

_____

_____

_____

The Sticky Solution

Improvement isn't inevitable. Change is.

UNKNOWN

Congratulations! You have just committed to five consecutive days of sticking with this journal. It is a commonly held notion that if you push through resistance and take specific action for a number of days in a row, it becomes an established habit. To give you a head start and ensure that you are sticking with it, here is a healthy push to help you make sure this habit sticks:

The Bad News: Research in 2010 has showed that 88% of people who make New Year's Resolutions fail to keep them.[6]

The Good News: You are better than that. You have already taken more steps than most to ensure you are on the right track.

The Better News: You will be getting tips and tricks to bulletproof your commitment in the following pages.

TRUTH & ACTIONS
*How do I know I'm better today
compared to three years ago?*

You don't, unless you are keeping track. It's all too common to assume that we're clearer, more mature, smarter and wiser in our forties than in our teens. An ignorant twenty-something is likely to end up a spectacularly ignorant eighty-something. Conversely, an intelligent teenager intent on seeking wisdom might reliably end up as a wise, oracular sixty-something. The difference? Read on.

TRUTH NUMBER 1
*Minuscule activities lead to massive
improvements (and setbacks).*

That job fair gets you your dream job. A new friend devoted to fitness inspires you to train regularly, getting you in the best shape of your life. Starting your mornings off on the right foot leads to the most productive days you have ever had. That is the objective of the journal you are holding.

Alas, all changes are not positive. That traffic jam to the interview crushes your dream job opportunity. An irate family member keeps you up at night, replaying nightmarish scenarios of what you should have said or done.

Fortunately, the universe isn't all chaos. Through it all, there are always patterns, guiding lines, and natural rhythms that yearn to be discovered by the penetrating mind. This is liberating.

TRUTH NUMBER 2
*If you're not moving forward, you're most likely moving
backwards. There is no standing still in life.*

Unless you methodically track and do a complete analysis of your day, figuring out what is effective and what is not, your daily activities are not much different from a cow's unconscious grazing on the field. There is no clear purpose, no guiding light that strings your actions together—they are steeped in unconsciousness.

Grow through reflection.

LIBERATING TRUTH NUMBER 3

The right action is the universal problem solver.

Sit down with a cup of your favorite beverage. Proceed to reflect on the following questions:

WHAT IS YOUR BIGGEST CHALLENGE?

This can be anything from creating a better relationship to feeling comfortable in your own skin to becoming more financially stable. Chances are there is something that is on your mind most of the time.

Put it on paper.

_____

_____

_____

WHAT IS ONE IDENTITY STATEMENT THAT WOULD CHANGE EVERYTHING FOR YOU?

Create an identity statement that remedies the above challenge. Every challenge has a remedy. Use this statement in your journal. Stick with this statement until it becomes true in your life. Read the preceding statement again. Engrave it in your mind before moving ahead.

EXAMPLES

I am giving and receiving of profound love and respect.

I am always surrounding myself with people who have a positive influence in my personal growth journey.

I am taking time to practice self love to promote a positive relationship with my body; emotionally, mentally and physically.

Your Identity Statement

Write your identity statement.

_____

_____

_____

_____

_____

What are three major obstacles that would stop you from
writing the journal (morning/night)?

1. _____

2. _____

3. _____

Write two actions you can take per obstacle to
ensure that your resistance doesn't overpower your will.

1. _____

_____

2. _____

_____

3. _____

_____

The key to growth is to learn to make promises and to *keep them*.

STEPHEN R. COVEY

Accountability

Choose a way to keep yourself accountable for writing the journal.

Immerse yourself in tips, videos, and reminders by signing up to receive our curated series of emails designed specifically for The Five Minute Journal owners like you. Go to journalhabit.com to sign up.

Pick a close friend or significant other you can rely on to check on you daily through text—similar to an AA Sponsor. This can also work well if you have received this as a gift from a friend.

If you are more comfortable using pen and paper, just check off every day that you finish the journal in a calendar. There is nothing like a powerful visual reminder of commitment. You can use apps like coach.me or stickk.com to stay accountable.

Choose your method of accountability, and let's begin!

The Journal

Gratitude unlocks the fullness of life. It turns what we have into enough, and more. It turns denial into acceptance, chaos to order, confusion to clarity.

MELODY BEATTIE

I am grateful for...

1. The warm bed that I sleep in.
2. My body that is working in perfect harmony.
3. The incredible friends in my life.

What would make today great?

1. Taking extra time for myself before work.
2. Going for a walk after lunch.
3. Sleeping before 10.30 PM.

Daily affirmation

I am confident and comfortable in my own skin.

I am living with passion and purpose.

Highlights of the Day

1. I remembered to call my friend and we had a good chat.
2. A colleague recommended a wonderful book for me.
3. I saw a cute stranger at the cafe and sayed "Hi".

What did I learn today?

Communicating openly with my boss helps me avoid stress.

Working out in the morning makes me energized and happy.

*The only person you are destined to become
is the person you decide to be.*

RALPH WALDO EMERSON

I am grateful for...

1. _____
2. _____
3. _____

What would make today great?

1. _____
2. _____
3. _____

Daily affirmation

_____
_____

Highlights of the Day

1. _____
2. _____
3. _____

What did I learn today?

_____
_____

Happiness cannot be traveled to, owned, earned, worn or consumed. Happiness is the spiritual experience of living every minute with love, grace, and gratitude.

DENIS WAITLEY

I am grateful for...

1. _____
2. _____
3. _____

What would make today great?

1. _____
2. _____
3. _____

Daily affirmation

_____
_____

Highlights of the Day

1. _____
2. _____
3. _____

What did I learn today?

_____
_____

39

☼ .... / .... / 20 ......

*Write a text, email, or letter to someone
you truly care about.*

I am grateful for...

1. _____
2. _____
3. _____

What would make today great?

1. _____
2. _____
3. _____

Daily affirmation

_____
_____

☾

Highlights of the Day

1. _____
2. _____
3. _____

What did I learn today?

_____
_____

The best and most beautiful things in the world can't be seen or even touched, they must be felt with the heart.

HELEN KELLER

I am grateful for...

1. _____
2. _____
3. _____

What would make today great?

1. _____
2. _____
3. _____

Daily affirmation

_____

_____

Highlights of the Day

1. _____
2. _____
3. _____

What did I learn today?

_____

_____

☼

*What you do makes a difference, and you have to
decide what kind of difference you want to make.*
JANE GOODALL

I am grateful for...

1. _____
2. _____
3. _____

What would make today great?

1. _____
2. _____
3. _____

Daily affirmation

_____

_____

☾

Highlights of the Day

1. _____
2. _____
3. _____

What did I learn today?

_____

_____

My Commitment Review

Congratulations on reaching day 5! How was it for you? Take a few moments to reflect on how you've used The Five Minute Journal and how this has made you feel. Have you fulfilled your commitment to writing in the journal every morning and evening? Are you able to focus on the highlights of each day? Have you attended to your daily gratitudes and affirmations?

Think back to the commitment you made to yourself on page 29. How do you feel reading through your entries now? Remember that committing to this journal is the simplest, most effective thing you can do every day to be happier. And don't forget to reward yourself! Make sure to block out time in your schedule to follow this through and enjoy your reward—you've earned it.

Now that you've completed your first 5 days, you can confidently move forward with the The Five Minute Journal at your side. Here at Intelligent Change we know that community support is important to keep us on track, and that's why we have a wealth of resources and inspiration ready for you.

Head over to our Instagram page
@INTELLIGENTCHANGE *to join us.*

*There is something wonderfully bold and liberating
about saying yes to our entire imperfect and messy life.*

TARA BRACH

I am grateful for...

1. _____
2. _____
3. _____

What would make today great?

1. _____
2. _____
3. _____

Daily affirmation

_____

_____

Highlights of the Day

1. _____
2. _____
3. _____

What did I learn today?

_____

_____

*Once you begin to take note of the things you are grateful for,
you begin to lose sight of the things that you lack.*

GERMANY KENT

I am grateful for...

1. _____
2. _____
3. _____

What would make today great?

1. _____
2. _____
3. _____

Daily affirmation

_____

_____

Highlights of the Day

1. _____
2. _____
3. _____

What did I learn today?

_____

_____

☼

Every day may not be good, but there is
something good in every day.
ALICE MORSE EARLE

I am grateful for...

1. _____
2. _____
3. _____

What would make today great?

1. _____
2. _____
3. _____

Daily affirmation

_____

_____

☾

Highlights of the Day

1. _____
2. _____
3. _____

What did I learn today?

_____

_____

.... / .... / 20 .....

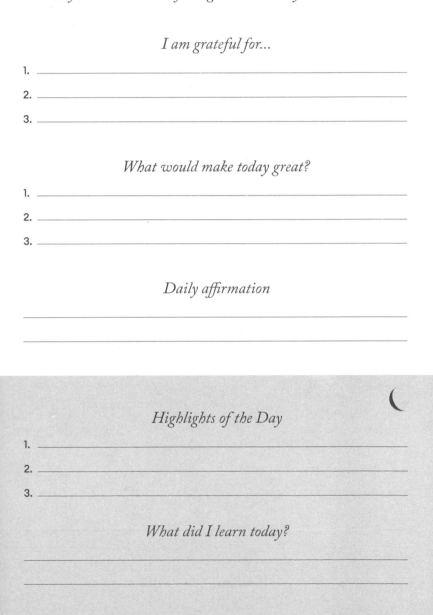

*Pause today for an extra few moments with each question to
really connect with the feeling behind what you write down.*

I am grateful for...

1. _____
2. _____
3. _____

What would make today great?

1. _____
2. _____
3. _____

Daily affirmation

_____

_____

Highlights of the Day

1. _____
2. _____
3. _____

What did I learn today?

_____

_____

47

*Give every day the chance to become
the most beautiful day of your life.*
MARK TWAIN

I am grateful for...

1. _____
2. _____
3. _____

What would make today great?

1. _____
2. _____
3. _____

Daily affirmation

_____
_____

☾

Highlights of the Day

1. _____
2. _____
3. _____

What did I learn today?

_____
_____

Being thankful is not always experienced as a natural state of existence, we must work at it, akin to a type of strength training for the heart.

LARISSA GOMEZ

I am grateful for...

1. _____
2. _____
3. _____

What would make today great?

1. _____
2. _____
3. _____

Daily affirmation

_____

_____

Highlights of the Day

1. _____
2. _____
3. _____

What did I learn today?

_____

_____

It's not what you look at that matters, it's what you see.

HENRY DAVID THOREAU

I am grateful for...

1. _____
2. _____
3. _____

What would make today great?

1. _____
2. _____
3. _____

Daily affirmation

_____
_____

Highlights of the Day

1. _____
2. _____
3. _____

What did I learn today?

_____
_____

Life is a song—sing it. Life is a game—play it.
Life is a challenge—meet it. Life is a dream—realize it.
Life is love—enjoy it.

SAI BABA

I am grateful for...

1. _____
2. _____
3. _____

What would make today great?

1. _____
2. _____
3. _____

Daily affirmation

_____

_____

Highlights of the Day

1. _____
2. _____
3. _____

What did I learn today?

_____

_____

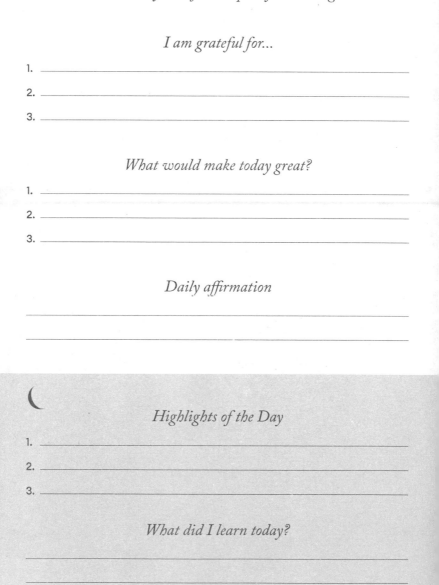

WEEKLY CHALLENGE

*This week, wake up 10 minutes earlier and spend
some time with yourself in the peaceful morning hours.*

I am grateful for...

1. _____
2. _____
3. _____

What would make today great?

1. _____
2. _____
3. _____

Daily affirmation

_____

_____

Highlights of the Day

1. _____
2. _____
3. _____

What did I learn today?

_____

_____

We need to live the best that's in us.
ANGELA BASSETT

I am grateful for...

1. _____
2. _____
3. _____

What would make today great?

1. _____
2. _____
3. _____

Daily affirmation

_____
_____

Highlights of the Day

1. _____
2. _____
3. _____

What did I learn today?

_____
_____

*As we express our gratitude, we must never forget that
the highest appreciation is not to utter words,
but to live by them.*

JOHN F. KENNEDY

I am grateful for...

1. _____
2. _____
3. _____

What would make today great?

1. _____
2. _____
3. _____

Daily affirmation

_____
_____

Highlights of the Day

1. _____
2. _____
3. _____

What did I learn today?

_____
_____

Put your heart, mind, and soul into even your smallest acts.
This is the secret of success.
SWAMI SIVANANDA

I am grateful for...

1. _____
2. _____
3. _____

What would make today great?

1. _____
2. _____
3. _____

Daily affirmation

_____

_____

Highlights of the Day

1. _____
2. _____
3. _____

What did I learn today?

_____

_____

Never be limited by other people's limited imaginations.

DR. MAE JEMISON

I am grateful for...

1. _____
2. _____
3. _____

What would make today great?

1. _____
2. _____
3. _____

Daily affirmation

_____
_____

Highlights of the Day

1. _____
2. _____
3. _____

What did I learn today?

_____
_____

*Once we recognize we can feel deeply, love deeply, can feel joy,
then we will demand that all parts of our lives
produce that kind of joy.*

AUDRE LORDE

I am grateful for...

1. _____
2. _____
3. _____

What would make today great?

1. _____
2. _____
3. _____

Daily affirmation

_____
_____

Highlights of the Day

1. _____
2. _____
3. _____

What did I learn today?

_____
_____

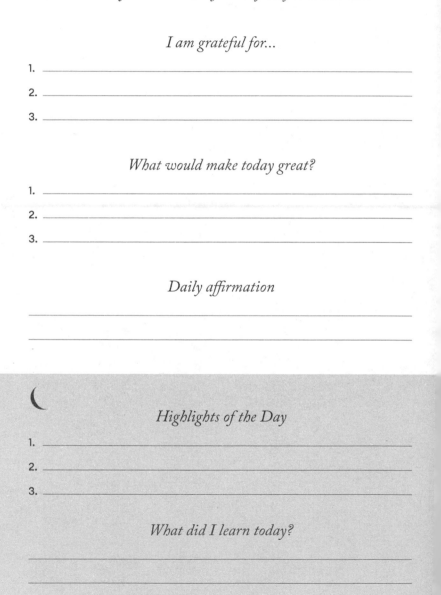

WEEKLY CHALLENGE

*Movement is key to your well-being. Today, take stairs
instead of an elevator, or find any way to walk more.*

I am grateful for...

1. _____
2. _____
3. _____

What would make today great?

1. _____
2. _____
3. _____

Daily affirmation

_____
_____

Highlights of the Day

1. _____
2. _____
3. _____

What did I learn today?

_____
_____

Change your thoughts and you change your world.
NORMAN VINCENT PEALE

I am grateful for...

1. _____
2. _____
3. _____

What would make today great?

1. _____
2. _____
3. _____

Daily affirmation

_____
_____

Highlights of the Day

1. _____
2. _____
3. _____

What did I learn today?

_____
_____

You cannot get an A if you're afraid of getting an F.

QUINCY JONES

I am grateful for...

1. _____
2. _____
3. _____

What would make today great?

1. _____
2. _____
3. _____

Daily affirmation

_____

_____

Highlights of the Day

1. _____
2. _____
3. _____

What did I learn today?

_____

_____

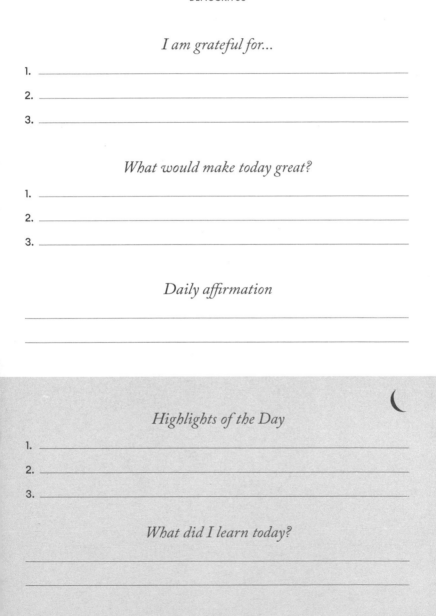

*Happiness resides not in possessions, and not in gold,
happiness dwells in the soul.*

DEMOCRITUS

I am grateful for...

1.
2.
3.

What would make today great?

1.
2.
3.

Daily affirmation

Highlights of the Day

1.
2.
3.

What did I learn today?

*Life is about not knowing, having to change,
taking the moment and making the best of it,
without knowing what's going to happen next.*

GILDA RADNER

I am grateful for...

1. _____
2. _____
3. _____

What would make today great?

1. _____
2. _____
3. _____

Daily affirmation

_____

_____

☾

Highlights of the Day

1. _____
2. _____
3. _____

What did I learn today?

_____

_____

*Sometimes if you want to see a change for the better,
you have to take things into your own hands.*
CLINT EASTWOOD

I am grateful for...

1. _____
2. _____
3. _____

What would make today great?

1. _____
2. _____
3. _____

Daily affirmation

_____

_____

Highlights of the Day

1. _____
2. _____
3. _____

What did I learn today?

_____

_____

☼

.... / .... / 20 ......

Be present in all things and thankful for all things.
MAYA ANGELOU

I am grateful for...

1. _____
2. _____
3. _____

What would make today great?

1. _____
2. _____
3. _____

Daily affirmation

_____
_____

☾

Highlights of the Day

1. _____
2. _____
3. _____

What did I learn today?

_____
_____

Look through your favorite old photos today.
Being nostalgic can boost your happiness.

I am grateful for...

1. _____
2. _____
3. _____

What would make today great?

1. _____
2. _____
3. _____

Daily affirmation

_____
_____

Highlights of the Day

1. _____
2. _____
3. _____

What did I learn today?

_____
_____

Life is a journey, and if you fall in love with the journey,
you will be in love forever.

PETER HAGERTY

I am grateful for...

1. _____
2. _____
3. _____

What would make today great?

1. _____
2. _____
3. _____

Daily affirmation

_____

_____

Highlights of the Day

1. _____
2. _____
3. _____

What did I learn today?

_____

_____

Caring for myself is not self-indulgence, it is self-preservation.
AUDRE LORDE

I am grateful for...

1. _____
2. _____
3. _____

What would make today great?

1. _____
2. _____
3. _____

Daily affirmation

_____
_____

Highlights of the Day

1. _____
2. _____
3. _____

What did I learn today?

_____
_____

Miracles happen everyday, change your perception of
what a miracle is and you'll see them all around you.

JON BON JOVI

I am grateful for...

1. _____
2. _____
3. _____

What would make today great?

1. _____
2. _____
3. _____

Daily affirmation

_____
_____

Highlights of the Day

1. _____
2. _____
3. _____

What did I learn today?

_____
_____

The best way to pay for a lovely moment is to enjoy it.
RICHARD BACH

I am grateful for...

1. _____
2. _____
3. _____

What would make today great?

1. _____
2. _____
3. _____

Daily affirmation

_____
_____

Highlights of the Day

1. _____
2. _____
3. _____

What did I learn today?

_____
_____

WEEKLY CHALLENGE
If you catch yourself complaining today—pause.
Take full ownership of what's happening in your life by
approaching this moment with a solution-oriented mindset.

I am grateful for...

1. _____
2. _____
3. _____

What would make today great?

1. _____
2. _____
3. _____

Daily affirmation

_____
_____

Highlights of the Day

1. _____
2. _____
3. _____

What did I learn today?

_____
_____

When you put love out in the world it travels,
and it can touch people and reach people in ways
that we never even expected.

LAVERNE COX

I am grateful for...

1. _____
2. _____
3. _____

What would make today great?

1. _____
2. _____
3. _____

Daily affirmation

_____

_____

Highlights of the Day

1. _____
2. _____
3. _____

What did I learn today?

_____

_____

*Nothing new can come into your life unless
you are grateful for what you already have.*
MICHAEL BERNARD

I am grateful for...

1. _____
2. _____
3. _____

What would make today great?

1. _____
2. _____
3. _____

Daily affirmation

_____
_____

Highlights of the Day

1. _____
2. _____
3. _____

What did I learn today?

_____
_____

*I could choose to believe that in every day, in all things,
no matter how dark and ugly, there are shards of beauty
if I look for them.*

ANNA WHITE

I am grateful for...

1. _____
2. _____
3. _____

What would make today great?

1. _____
2. _____
3. _____

Daily affirmation

_____
_____

Highlights of the Day

1. _____
2. _____
3. _____

What did I learn today?

_____
_____

☼

*Connect, create meaning, make a difference,
matter, be missed.*

SETH GODIN

I am grateful for...

1. _____
2. _____
3. _____

What would make today great?

1. _____
2. _____
3. _____

Daily affirmation

_____

_____

☾

Highlights of the Day

1. _____
2. _____
3. _____

What did I learn today?

_____

_____

.... / .... / 20 ....

Take a break from social media today.
Reflect in the evening if it made you feel better to not scroll.

I am grateful for...

1. _____
2. _____
3. _____

What would make today great?

1. _____
2. _____
3. _____

Daily affirmation

_____
_____

Highlights of the Day

1. _____
2. _____
3. _____

What did I learn today?

_____
_____

☼

Dreams are today's answers to tomorrow's questions.
EDGAR CAYCE

I am grateful for...

1. _____
2. _____
3. _____

What would make today great?

1. _____
2. _____
3. _____

Daily affirmation

_____
_____

☾

Highlights of the Day

1. _____
2. _____
3. _____

What did I learn today?

_____
_____

Don't wait for someone to inspire you.
Go out and inspire the world.
MIMI IKONN

I am grateful for...

1. _____
2. _____
3. _____

What would make today great?

1. _____
2. _____
3. _____

Daily affirmation

_____
_____

Highlights of the Day

1. _____
2. _____
3. _____

What did I learn today?

_____
_____

Do your little bit of good where you are; it's those little bits
of good put together that overwhelm the world.

DESMOND TUTU

I am grateful for...

1. _____
2. _____
3. _____

What would make today great?

1. _____
2. _____
3. _____

Daily affirmation

_____

_____

Highlights of the Day

1. _____
2. _____
3. _____

What did I learn today?

_____

_____

In a gentle way, you can shake the world.

MAHATMA GANDHI

I am grateful for...

1. _____
2. _____
3. _____

What would make today great?

1. _____
2. _____
3. _____

Daily affirmation

_____

_____

Highlights of the Day

1. _____
2. _____
3. _____

What did I learn today?

_____

_____

☼   .... / .... / 20 ......

A song that always boosts my mood is _____.
Listen and dance to it today.

I am grateful for...

1. _____
2. _____
3. _____

What would make today great?

1. _____
2. _____
3. _____

Daily affirmation

_____
_____

☾

Highlights of the Day

1. _____
2. _____
3. _____

What did I learn today?

_____
_____

*Never let the fear of striking out
keep you from playing the game.*
BABE RUTH

I am grateful for...

1. _____
2. _____
3. _____

What would make today great?

1. _____
2. _____
3. _____

Daily affirmation

_____
_____

Highlights of the Day

1. _____
2. _____
3. _____

What did I learn today?

_____
_____

I will not follow where the path may lead, but I will go
where there is no path, and I will leave a trail.
MURIEL STRODE

I am grateful for...

1. _____
2. _____
3. _____

What would make today great?

1. _____
2. _____
3. _____

Daily affirmation

_____
_____

Highlights of the Day

1. _____
2. _____
3. _____

What did I learn today?

_____
_____

*Very often a change of self is needed more
than a change of scene.*

A. C. BENSON

I am grateful for...

1. _____
2. _____
3. _____

What would make today great?

1. _____
2. _____
3. _____

Daily affirmation

_____
_____

Highlights of the Day

1. _____
2. _____
3. _____

What did I learn today?

_____
_____

Challenges are what make life interesting and
overcoming them is what makes life meaningful.
JOSHUA J. MARINE

I am grateful for...

1. _____
2. _____
3. _____

What would make today great?

1. _____
2. _____
3. _____

Daily affirmation

_____
_____

Highlights of the Day

1. _____
2. _____
3. _____

What did I learn today?

_____
_____

Don't be afraid. Be focused. Be determined.
Be hopeful. Be empowered.
MICHELLE OBAMA

I am grateful for...

1. _____
2. _____
3. _____

What would make today great?

1. _____
2. _____
3. _____

Daily affirmation

_____
_____

Highlights of the Day

1. _____
2. _____
3. _____

What did I learn today?

_____
_____

*Even if we don't have the power to choose where
we come from, we can still choose where we go from there.*
STEPHEN CHBOSKY

I am grateful for...

1. _____
2. _____
3. _____

What would make today great?

1. _____
2. _____
3. _____

Daily affirmation

_____
_____

Highlights of the Day

1. _____
2. _____
3. _____

What did I learn today?

_____
_____

WEEKLY CHALLENGE
Put pen to paper and write a thank you card to someone special.

I am grateful for...

1. _____
2. _____
3. _____

What would make today great?

1. _____
2. _____
3. _____

Daily affirmation

_____

_____

Highlights of the Day

1. _____
2. _____
3. _____

What did I learn today?

_____

_____

☀

.... / .... / 20 ......

It is impossible to get better and look good at the same time.
Give yourself permission to be a beginner.

JULIA CAMERON

I am grateful for...

1. _____
2. _____
3. _____

What would make today great?

1. _____
2. _____
3. _____

Daily affirmation

_____
_____

☾

Highlights of the Day

1. _____
2. _____
3. _____

What did I learn today?

_____
_____

*The art of peaceful living comes down to living
compassionately and wisely.*

ALLAN LOKOS

I am grateful for...

1. _____
2. _____
3. _____

What would make today great?

1. _____
2. _____
3. _____

Daily affirmation

_____
_____

Highlights of the Day

1. _____
2. _____
3. _____

What did I learn today?

_____
_____

The more you like yourself, the less you are like anyone else, which makes you unique.

WALT DISNEY

I am grateful for...

1. _____
2. _____
3. _____

What would make today great?

1. _____
2. _____
3. _____

Daily affirmation

_____
_____

Highlights of the Day

1. _____
2. _____
3. _____

What did I learn today?

_____
_____

*Always remember, you have within you the strength,
the patience and the passion to reach for the stars
to change the world.*

HARRIET TUBMAN

I am grateful for...

1. _____
2. _____
3. _____

What would make today great?

1. _____
2. _____
3. _____

Daily affirmation

_____
_____

Highlights of the Day

1. _____
2. _____
3. _____

What did I learn today?

_____
_____

We are what our thoughts have made us;
so take care about what you think. Words are secondary.
Thoughts live; they travel far.

SWAMI VIVEKANANDA

I am grateful for...

1. _____
2. _____
3. _____

What would make today great?

1. _____
2. _____
3. _____

Daily affirmation

_____

_____

Highlights of the Day

1. _____
2. _____
3. _____

What did I learn today?

_____

_____

There is a calmness to a life lived in gratitude, a quiet joy.
RALPH H. BLUM

I am grateful for...

1. _____
2. _____
3. _____

What would make today great?

1. _____
2. _____
3. _____

Daily affirmation

_____
_____

Highlights of the Day

1. _____
2. _____
3. _____

What did I learn today?

_____
_____

.... / .... / 20......

Listen to your inner dialogue today and be mindful to use kind words and positive affirmations towards yourself.

I am grateful for...

1. _____
2. _____
3. _____

What would make today great?

1. _____
2. _____
3. _____

Daily affirmation

_____
_____

Highlights of the Day

1. _____
2. _____
3. _____

What did I learn today?

_____
_____

*Your life is your story, and the adventure ahead of you
is the journey to fulfill your own purpose and potential.*
KERRY WASHINGTON

I am grateful for...

1. _____
2. _____
3. _____

What would make today great?

1. _____
2. _____
3. _____

Daily affirmation

_____

_____

Highlights of the Day

1. _____
2. _____
3. _____

What did I learn today?

_____

_____

*I'm not interested in whether the glass is half empty
or half full. I'm interested in figuring out how to fill the glass.*
DONALD KABERUKA

I am grateful for...

1. _____
2. _____
3. _____

What would make today great?

1. _____
2. _____
3. _____

Daily affirmation

_____
_____

Highlights of the Day

1. _____
2. _____
3. _____

What did I learn today?

_____
_____

☼

Very little is needed to make a happy life;
it's all within yourself, in your way of thinking.
MARCUS AURELIUS

I am grateful for...

1. _____
2. _____
3. _____

What would make today great?

1. _____
2. _____
3. _____

Daily affirmation

_____
_____

☾

Highlights of the Day

1. _____
2. _____
3. _____

What did I learn today?

_____
_____

_____ / _____ / 20 _____

*The future belongs to those who believe
in the beauty of their dreams.*
ELEANOR ROOSEVELT

I am grateful for...

1. _____
2. _____
3. _____

What would make today great?

1. _____
2. _____
3. _____

Daily affirmation

_____
_____

☾

Highlights of the Day

1. _____
2. _____
3. _____

What did I learn today?

_____
_____

98

*The main thing is the YOU beneath the clothes and skin—
the ability to do, the will to conquer, the determination to
understand and know this great, wonderful, curious world.*

W. E. B. DU BOIS

I am grateful for...

1. _____
2. _____
3. _____

What would make today great?

1. _____
2. _____
3. _____

Daily affirmation

_____
_____

Highlights of the Day

1. _____
2. _____
3. _____

What did I learn today?

_____
_____

WEEKLY CHALLENGE
Someone I want to get to know better is
_____. *Invite them for a coffee/tea.*

I am grateful for...

1. _____
2. _____
3. _____

What would make today great?

1. _____
2. _____
3. _____

Daily affirmation

_____
_____

Highlights of the Day

1. _____
2. _____
3. _____

What did I learn today?

_____
_____

*All that happens to us, including our humiliations,
our misfortunes, our embarrassments, all is given to us
as raw material, as clay, so that we may shape our art.*

JORGE LUIS BORGES

I am grateful for...

1. _____
2. _____
3. _____

What would make today great?

1. _____
2. _____
3. _____

Daily affirmation

_____
_____

Highlights of the Day

1. _____
2. _____
3. _____

What did I learn today?

_____
_____

Taste every moment of your daily life.

THICH NHAT HANH

I am grateful for...

1. _____
2. _____
3. _____

What would make today great?

1. _____
2. _____
3. _____

Daily affirmation

_____
_____

Highlights of the Day

1. _____
2. _____
3. _____

What did I learn today?

_____
_____

Forever is composed of nows.
EMILY DICKINSON

I am grateful for...

1. _____
2. _____
3. _____

What would make today great?

1. _____
2. _____
3. _____

Daily affirmation

_____
_____

Highlights of the Day

1. _____
2. _____
3. _____

What did I learn today?

_____
_____

Strive not to be a success, but rather to be of value.

ALBERT EINSTEIN

I am grateful for...

1. _____
2. _____
3. _____

What would make today great?

1. _____
2. _____
3. _____

Daily affirmation

_____

_____

Highlights of the Day

1. _____
2. _____
3. _____

What did I learn today?

_____

_____

You always have a choice: to be a victim or to take responsibility for your life and show appreciation for everything you have, even when you think you don't have anything.

ALEX IKONN

I am grateful for...

1. _____
2. _____
3. _____

What would make today great?

1. _____
2. _____
3. _____

Daily affirmation

_____
_____

Highlights of the Day

1. _____
2. _____
3. _____

What did I learn today?

_____
_____

☼   .... / .... / 20......

A positive habit I want to implement into my life is
_____. *Start today.*

I am grateful for...

1. _____
2. _____
3. _____

What would make today great?

1. _____
2. _____
3. _____

Daily affirmation

_____

_____

☾

Highlights of the Day

1. _____
2. _____
3. _____

What did I learn today?

_____

_____

Dreams are the seeds of change. Nothing ever grows without a seed, and nothing ever changes without a dream.

DEBBY BOONE

I am grateful for...

1. _____
2. _____
3. _____

What would make today great?

1. _____
2. _____
3. _____

Daily affirmation

_____

_____

Highlights of the Day

1. _____
2. _____
3. _____

What did I learn today?

_____

_____

It is during our darkest moments that
we must focus to see the light.
ARISTOTLE

I am grateful for...

1. _____
2. _____
3. _____

What would make today great?

1. _____
2. _____
3. _____

Daily affirmation

_____
_____

Highlights of the Day

1. _____
2. _____
3. _____

What did I learn today?

_____
_____

The secret of happiness is freedom,
the secret of freedom is courage.
CARRIE JONES

I am grateful for...

1. _____
2. _____
3. _____

What would make today great?

1. _____
2. _____
3. _____

Daily affirmation

_____

_____

Highlights of the Day

1. _____
2. _____
3. _____

What did I learn today?

_____

_____

Become everything that one is capable of becoming.
ABRAHAM MASLOW

I am grateful for...

1. _____
2. _____
3. _____

What would make today great?

1. _____
2. _____
3. _____

Daily affirmation

_____

_____

Highlights of the Day

1. _____
2. _____
3. _____

What did I learn today?

_____

_____

☼

Someone I deeply care about is _____. Call or message them to say what makes them special to you. Just because.

I am grateful for...

1. _____
2. _____
3. _____

What would make today great?

1. _____
2. _____
3. _____

Daily affirmation

_____

_____

☾

Highlights of the Day

1. _____
2. _____
3. _____

What did I learn today?

_____

_____

☼

*If everything was perfect, you would never learn
and you would never grow.*

BEYONCÉ KNOWLES

I am grateful for...

1. _____
2. _____
3. _____

What would make today great?

1. _____
2. _____
3. _____

Daily affirmation

_____
_____

☾

Highlights of the Day

1. _____
2. _____
3. _____

What did I learn today?

_____
_____

☼

*Choosing to be positive and having a grateful attitude
is going to determine how you're going to live your life.*

JOEL OSTEND

I am grateful for...

1. _____
2. _____
3. _____

What would make today great?

1. _____
2. _____
3. _____

Daily affirmation

_____

_____

☾

Highlights of the Day

1. _____
2. _____
3. _____

What did I learn today?

_____

_____

I think being in love with life is a key to eternal youth.
DOUG HUTCHISON

I am grateful for...

1. _____
2. _____
3. _____

What would make today great?

1. _____
2. _____
3. _____

Daily affirmation

_____
_____

Highlights of the Day

1. _____
2. _____
3. _____

What did I learn today?

_____
_____

Light tomorrow with today.
ELIZABETH BARRETT BROWNING

I am grateful for...

1. _____
2. _____
3. _____

What would make today great?

1. _____
2. _____
3. _____

Daily affirmation

_____
_____

Highlights of the Day

1. _____
2. _____
3. _____

What did I learn today?

_____
_____

When we are no longer able to change a situation,
we are challenged to change ourselves.

VIKTOR E. FRANKL

I am grateful for...

1. _____
2. _____
3. _____

What would make today great?

1. _____
2. _____
3. _____

Daily affirmation

_____
_____

Highlights of the Day

1. _____
2. _____
3. _____

What did I learn today?

_____
_____

Walk 10.000 steps today.

I am grateful for...

1. _____
2. _____
3. _____

What would make today great?

1. _____
2. _____
3. _____

Daily affirmation

_____
_____

Highlights of the Day

1. _____
2. _____
3. _____

What did I learn today?

_____
_____

A happy life consists in tranquility of mind.
CICERO

I am grateful for...

1. _____
2. _____
3. _____

What would make today great?

1. _____
2. _____
3. _____

Daily affirmation

_____

_____

Highlights of the Day

1. _____
2. _____
3. _____

What did I learn today?

_____

_____

118

If you feel like there's something out there that you're supposed to be doing, if you have a passion for it, then stop wishing and just do it.

WANDA SYKES

I am grateful for...

1. _____
2. _____
3. _____

What would make today great?

1. _____
2. _____
3. _____

Daily affirmation

_____
_____

Highlights of the Day

1. _____
2. _____
3. _____

What did I learn today?

_____
_____

Thankfulness is the quickest path to joy.
JEFFERSON BETHKE

I am grateful for...

1. _____
2. _____
3. _____

What would make today great?

1. _____
2. _____
3. _____

Daily affirmation

_____

_____

Highlights of the Day

1. _____
2. _____
3. _____

What did I learn today?

_____

_____

We must discover the power of love, the redemptive power of love.
And when we discover that, we will be able to make of this
old world a new world. Love is the only way.

MARTIN LUTHER KING JR.

I am grateful for...

1. _____
2. _____
3. _____

What would make today great?

1. _____
2. _____
3. _____

Daily affirmation

_____

_____

Highlights of the Day

1. _____
2. _____
3. _____

What did I learn today?

_____

_____

The most beautiful things are memories and moments.
If you don't celebrate those, they can pass you by.
ALEK WEK

I am grateful for...

1. _____
2. _____
3. _____

What would make today great?

1. _____
2. _____
3. _____

Daily affirmation

_____
_____

☾

Highlights of the Day

1. _____
2. _____
3. _____

What did I learn today?

_____
_____

It is not in the stars to hold our destiny but in ourselves.
WILLIAM SHAKESPEARE

I am grateful for...

1. _____
2. _____
3. _____

What would make today great?

1. _____
2. _____
3. _____

Daily affirmation

_____

_____

Highlights of the Day

1. _____
2. _____
3. _____

What did I learn today?

_____

_____

☼

WEEKLY CHALLENGE
Do one random act of kindness today and make someone's day.

I am grateful for...

1. _____
2. _____
3. _____

What would make today great?

1. _____
2. _____
3. _____

Daily affirmation

_____
_____

☾

Highlights of the Day

1. _____
2. _____
3. _____

What did I learn today?

_____
_____

*Champions are made from something they have
deep inside them: a desire, a dream, a vision.*

MUHAMMAD ALI

I am grateful for...

1. _____
2. _____
3. _____

What would make today great?

1. _____
2. _____
3. _____

Daily affirmation

_____
_____

Highlights of the Day

1. _____
2. _____
3. _____

What did I learn today?

_____
_____

That's life: starting over, one breath at a time.

SHARON SALZBERG

I am grateful for...

1. _____
2. _____
3. _____

What would make today great?

1. _____
2. _____
3. _____

Daily affirmation

_____
_____

Highlights of the Day

1. _____
2. _____
3. _____

What did I learn today?

_____
_____

*Learn to enjoy every minute of your life. Be happy now.
Don't wait for something outside of yourself to make you
happy in the future.*

EARL NIGHTINGALE

I am grateful for...

1. _____
2. _____
3. _____

What would make today great?

1. _____
2. _____
3. _____

Daily affirmation

_____

_____

Highlights of the Day

1. _____
2. _____
3. _____

What did I learn today?

_____

_____

Being deeply loved by someone gives you strength,
while loving someone deeply gives you courage.
LAO TZU

I am grateful for...

1. _____

2. _____

3. _____

What would make today great?

1. _____

2. _____

3. _____

Daily affirmation

_____

_____

Highlights of the Day

1. _____

2. _____

3. _____

What did I learn today?

_____

_____

You do not find the happy life. You make it.
CAMILLA EYRING KIMBALL

I am grateful for...

1. _____
2. _____
3. _____

What would make today great?

1. _____
2. _____
3. _____

Daily affirmation

_____
_____

Highlights of the Day

1. _____
2. _____
3. _____

What did I learn today?

_____
_____

Always remember, your focus determines your reality.
GEORGE LUCAS

I am grateful for...

1. _____
2. _____
3. _____

What would make today great?

1. _____
2. _____
3. _____

Daily affirmation

_____
_____

☾

Highlights of the Day

1. _____
2. _____
3. _____

What did I learn today?

_____
_____

Bring some fresh air to your space. Rearrange your space, declutter your closet, and donate things you no longer need to a charitable organization.

I am grateful for...

1. _____
2. _____
3. _____

What would make today great?

1. _____
2. _____
3. _____

Daily affirmation

_____

_____

Highlights of the Day

1. _____
2. _____
3. _____

What did I learn today?

_____

_____

*Life is not so much what you accomplish
as what you overcome.*
ROBIN ROBERTS

I am grateful for...

1. _____
2. _____
3. _____

What would make today great?

1. _____
2. _____
3. _____

Daily affirmation

_____

_____

Highlights of the Day

1. _____
2. _____
3. _____

What did I learn today?

_____

_____

When we seek to discover the best in others,
we somehow bring out the best in ourselves.
WILLIAM ARTHUR WARD

I am grateful for...

1. _____
2. _____
3. _____

What would make today great?

1. _____
2. _____
3. _____

Daily affirmation

_____

_____

Highlights of the Day

1. _____
2. _____
3. _____

What did I learn today?

_____

_____

Life is short, and it is here to be lived.
KATE WINSLET

I am grateful for...

1. _____
2. _____
3. _____

What would make today great?

1. _____
2. _____
3. _____

Daily affirmation

_____
_____

Highlights of the Day

1. _____
2. _____
3. _____

What did I learn today?

_____
_____

Love does not dominate; it cultivates.

JOHANN WOLFGANG VON GOETHE

I am grateful for...

1. _____
2. _____
3. _____

What would make today great?

1. _____
2. _____
3. _____

Daily affirmation

_____

_____

Highlights of the Day

1. _____
2. _____
3. _____

What did I learn today?

_____

_____

You are never too old to set
another goal or to dream a new dream.
C.S. LEWIS

I am grateful for...

1. _____
2. _____
3. _____

What would make today great?

1. _____
2. _____
3. _____

Daily affirmation

_____
_____

Highlights of the Day

1. _____
2. _____
3. _____

What did I learn today?

_____
_____

Finding beauty in a broken world
is creating beauty in the world we find.
TERRY TEMPEST WILLIAMS

I am grateful for...

1. _____
2. _____
3. _____

What would make today great?

1. _____
2. _____
3. _____

Daily affirmation

_____
_____

Highlights of the Day

1. _____
2. _____
3. _____

What did I learn today?

_____
_____

Boost someone else's confidence and give a genuine compliment
to someone you see, talk to, or think about today.

I am grateful for...

1. _____
2. _____
3. _____

What would make today great?

1. _____
2. _____
3. _____

Daily affirmation

_____
_____

Highlights of the Day

1. _____
2. _____
3. _____

What did I learn today?

_____
_____

Calmness of mind is one of the beautiful jewels of wisdom.
JAMES ALLEN

I am grateful for...

1. _____
2. _____
3. _____

What would make today great?

1. _____
2. _____
3. _____

Daily affirmation

_____

_____

Highlights of the Day

1. _____
2. _____
3. _____

What did I learn today?

_____

_____

Life isn't about finding yourself.
Life is about creating yourself.
GEORGE BERNARD SHAW

I am grateful for...

1. _____
2. _____
3. _____

What would make today great?

1. _____
2. _____
3. _____

Daily affirmation

_____
_____

Highlights of the Day

1. _____
2. _____
3. _____

What did I learn today?

_____
_____

Knowing yourself is life's eternal homework.
FELICIA DAY

I am grateful for...

1. _____
2. _____
3. _____

What would make today great?

1. _____
2. _____
3. _____

Daily affirmation

_____
_____

Highlights of the Day

1. _____
2. _____
3. _____

What did I learn today?

_____
_____

The secret to living the life of your dreams is to start living the life of your dreams today, in every little way you possibly can.

MIKE DOOLEY

I am grateful for...

1. _____
2. _____
3. _____

What would make today great?

1. _____
2. _____
3. _____

Daily affirmation

_____
_____

Highlights of the Day

1. _____
2. _____
3. _____

What did I learn today?

_____
_____

☼

WEEKLY CHALLENGE

The new recipe I want to try out is _____.
Treat yourself to a delicious home-cooked meal and invite
friends over to make it even more memorable.

I am grateful for...

1. _____
2. _____
3. _____

What would make today great?

1. _____
2. _____
3. _____

Daily affirmation

_____
_____

☾

Highlights of the Day

1. _____
2. _____
3. _____

What did I learn today?

_____
_____

143

The only way to do great work is to love what you do.
If you haven't found it yet, keep looking. Don't settle.
STEVE JOBS

I am grateful for...

1. _____
2. _____
3. _____

What would make today great?

1. _____
2. _____
3. _____

Daily affirmation

_____

_____

Highlights of the Day

1. _____
2. _____
3. _____

What did I learn today?

_____

_____

The most beautiful people we have known are those who have known defeat, known suffering, known struggle, known loss, and have found their way out of those depths.

ELISABETH KÜBLER-ROSS

I am grateful for...

1. _____
2. _____
3. _____

What would make today great?

1. _____
2. _____
3. _____

Daily affirmation

_____
_____

Highlights of the Day

1. _____
2. _____
3. _____

What did I learn today?

_____
_____

*Nothing in the universe can stop you
from letting go and starting over.*
GUY FINLEY

I am grateful for...

1. _____
2. _____
3. _____

What would make today great?

1. _____
2. _____
3. _____

Daily affirmation

_____
_____

☾

Highlights of the Day

1. _____
2. _____
3. _____

What did I learn today?

_____
_____

The whole future lies in uncertainty:
live immediately.
SENECA

I am grateful for...

1. _____
2. _____
3. _____

What would make today great?

1. _____
2. _____
3. _____

Daily affirmation

_____

_____

Highlights of the Day

1. _____
2. _____
3. _____

What did I learn today?

_____

_____

Mistakes are a fact of life.
It is the response to the error that counts.
NIKKI GIOVANNI

I am grateful for...

1. _____
2. _____
3. _____

What would make today great?

1. _____
2. _____
3. _____

Daily affirmation

_____
_____

Highlights of the Day

1. _____
2. _____
3. _____

What did I learn today?

_____
_____

Somewhere inside all of us is the power to change the world.
ROALD DAHL

I am grateful for...

1. _____
2. _____
3. _____

What would make today great?

1. _____
2. _____
3. _____

Daily affirmation

_____
_____

Highlights of the Day

1. _____
2. _____
3. _____

What did I learn today?

_____
_____

WEEKLY CHALLENGE

Pick a topic you know nothing about and understand the fundamentals of it.

I am grateful for...

1. _____
2. _____
3. _____

What would make today great?

1. _____
2. _____
3. _____

Daily affirmation

_____

_____

Highlights of the Day

1. _____
2. _____
3. _____

What did I learn today?

_____

_____

☼

The measure of achievement is not winning awards.
It's doing something that you appreciate,
something you believe is worthwhile.

JULIA CHILD

I am grateful for...

1. _____
2. _____
3. _____

What would make today great?

1. _____
2. _____
3. _____

Daily affirmation

_____
_____

☾

Highlights of the Day

1. _____
2. _____
3. _____

What did I learn today?

_____
_____

Change will not come if we wait for some other person or some other time. We are the ones we've been waiting for. We are the change that we seek.

BARACK OBAMA

I am grateful for...

1. _____
2. _____
3. _____

What would make today great?

1. _____
2. _____
3. _____

Daily affirmation

_____
_____

Highlights of the Day

1. _____
2. _____
3. _____

What did I learn today?

_____
_____

*When we create peace, harmony and balance
in our minds, we'll find it in our lives.*
LOUISE HAY

I am grateful for...

1. _____
2. _____
3. _____

What would make today great?

1. _____
2. _____
3. _____

Daily affirmation

_____
_____

Highlights of the Day

1. _____
2. _____
3. _____

What did I learn today?

_____
_____

☼   .... / .... / 20 ......

The more you praise and celebrate your life,
the more there is in life to celebrate.
OPRAH WINFREY

I am grateful for...

1. _____
2. _____
3. _____

What would make today great?

1. _____
2. _____
3. _____

Daily affirmation

_____
_____

☾

Highlights of the Day

1. _____
2. _____
3. _____

What did I learn today?

_____
_____

☼

*My general attitude to life is to enjoy
every minute of every day.*
RICHARD BRANSON

I am grateful for...

1. _____
2. _____
3. _____

What would make today great?

1. _____
2. _____
3. _____

Daily affirmation

_____
_____

☾

Highlights of the Day

1. _____
2. _____
3. _____

What did I learn today?

_____
_____

*Mindfulness is a way of befriending
ourselves and our experience.*
JON KABAT-ZINN

I am grateful for...

1. _____
2. _____
3. _____

What would make today great?

1. _____
2. _____
3. _____

Daily affirmation

_____
_____

Highlights of the Day

1. _____
2. _____
3. _____

What did I learn today?

_____
_____

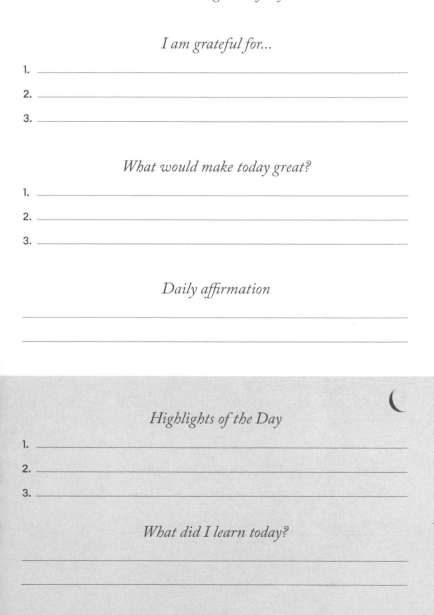

Make a list of your three recent accomplishments.
Celebrate and acknowledge how far you have come.

I am grateful for...

1. _____
2. _____
3. _____

What would make today great?

1. _____
2. _____
3. _____

Daily affirmation

_____
_____

Highlights of the Day

1. _____
2. _____
3. _____

What did I learn today?

_____
_____

You are the sky. Everything else is just the weather.
PEMA CHÖDRÖN

I am grateful for...

1. _____
2. _____
3. _____

What would make today great?

1. _____
2. _____
3. _____

Daily affirmation

_____

_____

Highlights of the Day

1. _____
2. _____
3. _____

What did I learn today?

_____

_____

*Looking at beauty in the world is the first step
of purifying the mind.*
AMIT RAY

I am grateful for...

1. _____
2. _____
3. _____

What would make today great?

1. _____
2. _____
3. _____

Daily affirmation

_____
_____

Highlights of the Day

1. _____
2. _____
3. _____

What did I learn today?

_____
_____

*People will forget what you said, people will forget
what you did, but people will never forget
how you made them feel.*

MAYA ANGELOU

I am grateful for...

1. _____
2. _____
3. _____

What would make today great?

1. _____
2. _____
3. _____

Daily affirmation

_____

_____

Highlights of the Day

1. _____
2. _____
3. _____

What did I learn today?

_____

_____

*Your vision will become clear only when
you look into your heart.*

CARL JUNG

I am grateful for...

1. _____
2. _____
3. _____

What would make today great?

1. _____
2. _____
3. _____

Daily affirmation

_____

_____

Highlights of the Day

1. _____
2. _____
3. _____

What did I learn today?

_____

_____

*Begin at once to live, and count each
separate day as a separate life.*

SENECA

I am grateful for...

1. _____
2. _____
3. _____

What would make today great?

1. _____
2. _____
3. _____

Daily affirmation

_____
_____

Highlights of the Day

1. _____
2. _____
3. _____

What did I learn today?

_____
_____

*Put your phone in a different room and read
for 30 minutes before going to sleep.*

I am grateful for...

1. _____
2. _____
3. _____

What would make today great?

1. _____
2. _____
3. _____

Daily affirmation

_____
_____

Highlights of the Day

1. _____
2. _____
3. _____

What did I learn today?

_____
_____

Be bold, be courageous, be your best.
GABRIELLE GIFFORDS

I am grateful for...

1. _____
2. _____
3. _____

What would make today great?

1. _____
2. _____
3. _____

Daily affirmation

_____

_____

Highlights of the Day

1. _____
2. _____
3. _____

What did I learn today?

_____

_____

Dreaming, after all, is a form of planning.
GLORIA STEINEM

I am grateful for...

1. _____
2. _____
3. _____

What would make today great?

1. _____
2. _____
3. _____

Daily affirmation

_____
_____

Highlights of the Day

1. _____
2. _____
3. _____

What did I learn today?

_____
_____

☼

*We must find time to stop and thank the people
who make a difference in our lives.*
JOHN F. KENNEDY

I am grateful for...

1. _____
2. _____
3. _____

What would make today great?

1. _____
2. _____
3. _____

Daily affirmation

_____
_____

☾

Highlights of the Day

1. _____
2. _____
3. _____

What did I learn today?

_____
_____

*If your actions inspire others to dream more, learn more,
do more, and become more, you are a leader.*

JOHN QUINCY ADAMS

I am grateful for...

1. _____
2. _____
3. _____

What would make today great?

1. _____
2. _____
3. _____

Daily affirmation

_____

_____

Highlights of the Day

1. _____
2. _____
3. _____

What did I learn today?

_____

_____

Documenting little details of your everyday life
becomes a celebration of who you are.

CAROLYN V. HAMILTON

I am grateful for...

1. _____
2. _____
3. _____

What would make today great?

1. _____
2. _____
3. _____

Daily affirmation

_____
_____

Highlights of the Day

1. _____
2. _____
3. _____

What did I learn today?

_____
_____

Anyone who has a why to live can bear almost any what.
FRIEDRICH NIETZSCHE

I am grateful for...

1. _____
2. _____
3. _____

What would make today great?

1. _____
2. _____
3. _____

Daily affirmation

_____

_____

Highlights of the Day

1. _____
2. _____
3. _____

What did I learn today?

_____

_____

✷

The funniest movie I've seen is _____.
Lift your spirit and watch it again this week.

I am grateful for...

1. _____

2. _____

3. _____

What would make today great?

1. _____

2. _____

3. _____

Daily affirmation

_____

_____

☾

Highlights of the Day

1. _____

2. _____

3. _____

What did I learn today?

_____

_____

Joy does not simply happen to us.
We have to choose joy and keep choosing it every day.

HENRI J.M. NOUWEN

I am grateful for...

1. _____
2. _____
3. _____

What would make today great?

1. _____
2. _____
3. _____

Daily affirmation

_____
_____

Highlights of the Day

1. _____
2. _____
3. _____

What did I learn today?

_____
_____

*After everything that's happened, how can
the world still be so beautiful? Because it is.*
MARGARET ATWOOD

I am grateful for...

1. _____
2. _____
3. _____

What would make today great?

1. _____
2. _____
3. _____

Daily affirmation

_____

_____

Highlights of the Day

1. _____
2. _____
3. _____

What did I learn today?

_____

_____

> *When things change inside you, things change around you.*
> LEWIS CARROLL

I am grateful for...

1. _____
2. _____
3. _____

What would make today great?

1. _____
2. _____
3. _____

Daily affirmation

_____

_____

Highlights of the Day

1. _____
2. _____
3. _____

What did I learn today?

_____

_____

We have two lives, and the second begins
when we realize we only have one.
CONFUCIUS

I am grateful for...

1. _____
2. _____
3. _____

What would make today great?

1. _____
2. _____
3. _____

Daily affirmation

_____

_____

Highlights of the Day

1. _____
2. _____
3. _____

What did I learn today?

_____

_____

Start each day with a grateful heart.
UNKNOWN

I am grateful for...

1. _____
2. _____
3. _____

What would make today great?

1. _____
2. _____
3. _____

Daily affirmation

_____
_____

Highlights of the Day

1. _____
2. _____
3. _____

What did I learn today?

_____
_____

☼

.... / .... / 20 ......

Only I can change my life. No one can do it for me.
CAROL BURNETT

I am grateful for...

1. _____
2. _____
3. _____

What would make today great?

1. _____
2. _____
3. _____

Daily affirmation

_____
_____

☾

Highlights of the Day

1. _____
2. _____
3. _____

What did I learn today?

_____
_____

176

WEEKLY CHALLENGE

Step out of your comfort zone and do something that scares you.
It can be talking to new people, asking for feedback, or
apologizing to someone.

I am grateful for...

1. _____
2. _____
3. _____

What would make today great?

1. _____
2. _____
3. _____

Daily affirmation

_____

_____

Highlights of the Day

1. _____
2. _____
3. _____

What did I learn today?

_____

_____

It's the possibility of having a dream come true
that makes life interesting.
PAULO COELHO

I am grateful for...

1. _____
2. _____
3. _____

What would make today great?

1. _____
2. _____
3. _____

Daily affirmation

_____
_____

Highlights of the Day

1. _____
2. _____
3. _____

What did I learn today?

_____
_____

Happiness is not doing fun things.
Happiness is doing meaningful things.
MAXIME LAGACÉ

I am grateful for...

1. _____
2. _____
3. _____

What would make today great?

1. _____
2. _____
3. _____

Daily affirmation

_____
_____

Highlights of the Day

1. _____
2. _____
3. _____

What did I learn today?

_____
_____

It's a wonderful thing to be optimistic.
It keeps you healthy and it keeps you resilient.
DANIEL KAHNEMAN

I am grateful for...

1. _____
2. _____
3. _____

What would make today great?

1. _____
2. _____
3. _____

Daily affirmation

_____
_____

Highlights of the Day

1. _____
2. _____
3. _____

What did I learn today?

_____
_____

Find a place inside where there's joy,
and the joy will burn out the pain.

JOSEPH CAMPBELL

I am grateful for...

1. _____
2. _____
3. _____

What would make today great?

1. _____
2. _____
3. _____

Daily affirmation

_____

_____

Highlights of the Day

1. _____
2. _____
3. _____

What did I learn today?

_____

_____

*There is always light, if only we're brave enough
to see it. If only we're brave enough to be it.*
AMANDA GORMAN

I am grateful for...

1. _____
2. _____
3. _____

What would make today great?

1. _____
2. _____
3. _____

Daily affirmation

_____

_____

Highlights of the Day

1. _____
2. _____
3. _____

What did I learn today?

_____

_____

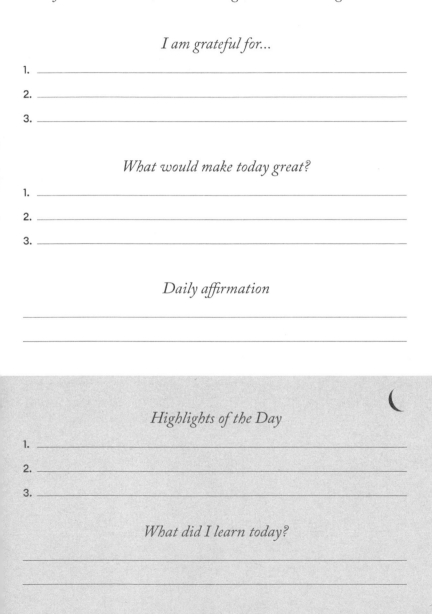

Take time to make yourself feel extra comfortable today.
Rest for an extra hour, book a massage, or eat an indulgent dessert.

I am grateful for...

1. _____
2. _____
3. _____

What would make today great?

1. _____
2. _____
3. _____

Daily affirmation

_____
_____

Highlights of the Day

1. _____
2. _____
3. _____

What did I learn today?

_____
_____

Gratitude and attitude are not challenges; they are choices.
ROBERT BRAATHE

I am grateful for...

1. _____
2. _____
3. _____

What would make today great?

1. _____
2. _____
3. _____

Daily affirmation

_____
_____

Highlights of the Day

1. _____
2. _____
3. _____

What did I learn today?

_____
_____

Keep your face to the sunshine and you cannot see a shadow.
HELEN KELLER

I am grateful for...

1. _____
2. _____
3. _____

What would make today great?

1. _____
2. _____
3. _____

Daily affirmation

_____
_____

Highlights of the Day

1. _____
2. _____
3. _____

What did I learn today?

_____
_____

What is fundamentally beautiful is compassion for yourself and those around you. That kind of beauty inflames the heart and enchants the soul.

LUPITA NYONG'O

I am grateful for...

1. _____
2. _____
3. _____

What would make today great?

1. _____
2. _____
3. _____

Daily affirmation

_____
_____

Highlights of the Day

1. _____
2. _____
3. _____

What did I learn today?

_____
_____

*Pleasure is always derived from something outside you,
whereas joy arises from within.*

ECKHART TOLLE

I am grateful for...

1. _____
2. _____
3. _____

What would make today great?

1. _____
2. _____
3. _____

Daily affirmation

_____

_____

Highlights of the Day

1. _____
2. _____
3. _____

What did I learn today?

_____

_____

☼ .... / .... / 20 ......

Beauty is when you can appreciate yourself.
When you love yourself, that's when you're most beautiful.
ZOE KRAVITZ

I am grateful for...

1. _____
2. _____
3. _____

What would make today great?

1. _____
2. _____
3. _____

Daily affirmation

_____
_____

☾ *Highlights of the Day*

1. _____
2. _____
3. _____

What did I learn today?

_____
_____

Everything you need is already inside.
BILL BOWERMAN

I am grateful for...

1. _____
2. _____
3. _____

What would make today great?

1. _____
2. _____
3. _____

Daily affirmation

_____
_____

Highlights of the Day

1. _____
2. _____
3. _____

What did I learn today?

_____
_____

WEEKLY CHALLENGE

Go out in nature, find a beautiful spot, and just sit there for awhile. Notice the beauty of this world.

I am grateful for...

1. _____
2. _____
3. _____

What would make today great?

1. _____
2. _____
3. _____

Daily affirmation

_____

_____

Highlights of the Day

1. _____
2. _____
3. _____

What did I learn today?

_____

_____

*Let us make our future now,
and let us make our dreams tomorrow's reality.*

MALALA YOUSAFZAI

I am grateful for...

1. _____
2. _____
3. _____

What would make today great?

1. _____
2. _____
3. _____

Daily affirmation

_____

_____

Highlights of the Day

1. _____
2. _____
3. _____

What did I learn today?

_____

_____

☼

I have found that if you love life, life will love you back.
ARTHUR RUBINSTEIN

I am grateful for...

1. _____
2. _____
3. _____

What would make today great?

1. _____
2. _____
3. _____

Daily affirmation

_____
_____

☾

Highlights of the Day

1. _____
2. _____
3. _____

What did I learn today?

_____
_____

*True freedom is understanding that we have a choice
in who and what we allow to have power over us.*

MERYL STREEP

I am grateful for...

1. _____
2. _____
3. _____

What would make today great?

1. _____
2. _____
3. _____

Daily affirmation

_____

_____

Highlights of the Day

1. _____
2. _____
3. _____

What did I learn today?

_____

_____

It's not the mountain that we conquer, but ourselves.
SIR EDMUND HILLARY

I am grateful for...

1. _____
2. _____
3. _____

What would make today great?

1. _____
2. _____
3. _____

Daily affirmation

_____

_____

Highlights of the Day

1. _____
2. _____
3. _____

What did I learn today?

_____

_____

One way to get the most out of life is to
look upon it as an adventure.

WILLIAM FEATHER

I am grateful for...

1. _____
2. _____
3. _____

What would make today great?

1. _____
2. _____
3. _____

Daily affirmation

_____

_____

Highlights of the Day

1. _____
2. _____
3. _____

What did I learn today?

_____

_____

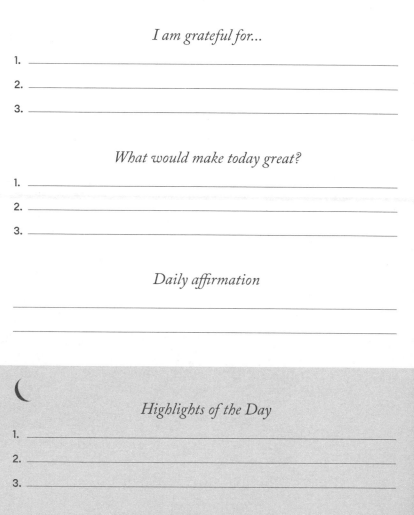

WEEKLY CHALLENGE

What is one cause you would like to support?
Do a kind deed and dedicate your time or resources to it.

I am grateful for...

1. _____
2. _____
3. _____

What would make today great?

1. _____
2. _____
3. _____

Daily affirmation

_____
_____

Highlights of the Day

1. _____
2. _____
3. _____

What did I learn today?

_____
_____

You don't always need a plan. Sometimes you just need to breathe, trust, let go, and see what happens.

MANDY HALE

I am grateful for...

1. _____
2. _____
3. _____

What would make today great?

1. _____
2. _____
3. _____

Daily affirmation

_____

_____

Highlights of the Day

1. _____
2. _____
3. _____

What did I learn today?

_____

_____

If you do things well, do them better.
Be daring, be first, be different, be just.
ANITA RODDICK

I am grateful for...

1. _____
2. _____
3. _____

What would make today great?

1. _____
2. _____
3. _____

Daily affirmation

_____
_____

Highlights of the Day

1. _____
2. _____
3. _____

What did I learn today?

_____
_____

Don't go through life, grow through life.

ERIC BUTTERWORTH

I am grateful for...

1. _____
2. _____
3. _____

What would make today great?

1. _____
2. _____
3. _____

Daily affirmation

_____

_____

Highlights of the Day

1. _____
2. _____
3. _____

What did I learn today?

_____

_____

☼

Action is the antidote to despair.
JOAN BAEZ

I am grateful for...

1. _____
2. _____
3. _____

What would make today great?

1. _____
2. _____
3. _____

Daily affirmation

_____
_____

☾

Highlights of the Day

1. _____
2. _____
3. _____

What did I learn today?

_____
_____

Dreams do not come true just because you dream them.
It's hard work that makes things happen.
It's hard work that creates change.

SHONDA RHIMES

I am grateful for...

1. _____
2. _____
3. _____

What would make today great?

1. _____
2. _____
3. _____

Daily affirmation

_____
_____

Highlights of the Day

1. _____
2. _____
3. _____

What did I learn today?

_____
_____

Very little is needed to make a happy life;
it's all within yourself, in your way of thinking.
MARCUS AURELIUS

I am grateful for...

1. _____
2. _____
3. _____

What would make today great?

1. _____
2. _____
3. _____

Daily affirmation

_____
_____

Highlights of the Day

1. _____
2. _____
3. _____

What did I learn today?

_____
_____

Don't focus on the pain. Focus on the progress.
DWAYNE JOHNSON

I am grateful for...

1. _____
2. _____
3. _____

What would make today great?

1. _____
2. _____
3. _____

Daily affirmation

_____
_____

Highlights of the Day

1. _____
2. _____
3. _____

What did I learn today?

_____
_____

☼

*Be less judgmental and practice love and understating
towards anyone and anything today.
How does it make you feel?*

I am grateful for...

1. _____

2. _____

3. _____

What would make today great?

1. _____

2. _____

3. _____

Daily affirmation

_____

_____

☾ *Highlights of the Day*

1. _____

2. _____

3. _____

What did I learn today?

_____

_____

*Real change, enduring change,
happens one step at a time.*
RUTH BADER GINSBURG

I am grateful for...

1. _____
2. _____
3. _____

What would make today great?

1. _____
2. _____
3. _____

Daily affirmation

_____
_____

Highlights of the Day

1. _____
2. _____
3. _____

What did I learn today?

_____
_____

.... / .... / 20......

It is never too late to be what you might have been.

GEORGE ELIOT

I am grateful for...

1. _____
2. _____
3. _____

What would make today great?

1. _____
2. _____
3. _____

Daily affirmation

_____
_____

☾

Highlights of the Day

1. _____
2. _____
3. _____

What did I learn today?

_____
_____

206

*There are two ways of spreading light:
to be the candle, or the mirror that reflects it.*

EDITH WHARTON

I am grateful for...

1. _____
2. _____
3. _____

What would make today great?

1. _____
2. _____
3. _____

Daily affirmation

_____

_____

Highlights of the Day

1. _____
2. _____
3. _____

What did I learn today?

_____

_____

Be the designer of your world and not merely the consumer of it.

JAMES CLEAR

I am grateful for...

1. _____
2. _____
3. _____

What would make today great?

1. _____
2. _____
3. _____

Daily affirmation

_____
_____

Highlights of the Day

1. _____
2. _____
3. _____

What did I learn today?

_____
_____

*I now see how owning our story and loving ourselves
through that process is the bravest thing that
we will ever do.*

BRENÉ BROWN

I am grateful for...

1. _____
2. _____
3. _____

What would make today great?

1. _____
2. _____
3. _____

Daily affirmation

_____
_____

Highlights of the Day

1. _____
2. _____
3. _____

What did I learn today?

_____
_____

209

The greatest of human emotions is love.
The most valuable of human gifts is the ability to learn.
Therefore learn to love.

UJ RAMDAS

I am grateful for...

1. _____
2. _____
3. _____

What would make today great?

1. _____
2. _____
3. _____

Daily affirmation

_____
_____

Highlights of the Day

1. _____
2. _____
3. _____

What did I learn today?

_____
_____

Listen genuinely to every person you have a conversation with today. Give them your undivided attention.

I am grateful for...

1. _____
2. _____
3. _____

What would make today great?

1. _____
2. _____
3. _____

Daily affirmation

_____

_____

Highlights of the Day

1. _____
2. _____
3. _____

What did I learn today?

_____

_____

There is only one happiness in this life, to love and be loved.
GEORGE SAND

I am grateful for...

1. _____
2. _____
3. _____

What would make today great?

1. _____
2. _____
3. _____

Daily affirmation

_____
_____

Highlights of the Day

1. _____
2. _____
3. _____

What did I learn today?

_____
_____

Sometimes, what you're looking for is already there.
ARETHA FRANKLIN

I am grateful for...

1. _____
2. _____
3. _____

What would make today great?

1. _____
2. _____
3. _____

Daily affirmation

_____
_____

Highlights of the Day

1. _____
2. _____
3. _____

What did I learn today?

_____
_____

*The choice isn't to move on—life moves whether
I want it to or not. No, the choice is to look forward.*
CAROLINE GEORGE

I am grateful for...

1. _____
2. _____
3. _____

What would make today great?

1. _____
2. _____
3. _____

Daily affirmation

_____

_____

☾

Highlights of the Day

1. _____
2. _____
3. _____

What did I learn today?

_____

_____

Every exit is an entry somewhere else.
TOM STOPPARD

I am grateful for...

1. _____
2. _____
3. _____

What would make today great?

1. _____
2. _____
3. _____

Daily affirmation

_____
_____

Highlights of the Day

1. _____
2. _____
3. _____

What did I learn today?

_____
_____

I feel that the simplicity of life is just being yourself.
BOBBY BROWN

I am grateful for...

1. _____
2. _____
3. _____

What would make today great?

1. _____
2. _____
3. _____

Daily affirmation

_____

_____

☾

Highlights of the Day

1. _____
2. _____
3. _____

What did I learn today?

_____

_____

We must be willing to let go of the life we have planned,
so as to have the life that is waiting for us.

E. M. FORSTER

I am grateful for...

1. _____
2. _____
3. _____

What would make today great?

1. _____
2. _____
3. _____

Daily affirmation

_____

_____

Highlights of the Day

1. _____
2. _____
3. _____

What did I learn today?

_____

_____

☼

WEEKLY CHALLENGE

One thing that always uplifts me is _____.
Do it today.

I am grateful for...

1. _____
2. _____
3. _____

What would make today great?

1. _____
2. _____
3. _____

Daily affirmation

_____
_____

☾

Highlights of the Day

1. _____
2. _____
3. _____

What did I learn today?

_____
_____

Happiness is the consequence of personal effort.
ELIZABETH GILBERT

I am grateful for...

1. _____
2. _____
3. _____

What would make today great?

1. _____
2. _____
3. _____

Daily affirmation

_____
_____

Highlights of the Day

1. _____
2. _____
3. _____

What did I learn today?

_____
_____

Visualization works if you work hard. That's the thing.
You can't just visualize and go eat a sandwich.

JIM CARREY

I am grateful for...

1. _____
2. _____
3. _____

What would make today great?

1. _____
2. _____
3. _____

Daily affirmation

_____
_____

Highlights of the Day

1. _____
2. _____
3. _____

What did I learn today?

_____
_____

My mission in life is not merely to survive, but to thrive;
and to do so with some passion, some compassion,
some humor, and some style.

MAYA ANGELOU

I am grateful for...

1. _____
2. _____
3. _____

What would make today great?

1. _____
2. _____
3. _____

Daily affirmation

_____
_____

Highlights of the Day

1. _____
2. _____
3. _____

What did I learn today?

_____
_____

Life has no limitations, except the ones you make.
LES BROWN

I am grateful for...

1. _____
2. _____
3. _____

What would make today great?

1. _____
2. _____
3. _____

Daily affirmation

_____
_____

Highlights of the Day

1. _____
2. _____
3. _____

What did I learn today?

_____
_____

Experience is not what happens to you;
it is what you do with what happens to you.
ALDOUS HUXLEY

I am grateful for...

1. _____
2. _____
3. _____

What would make today great?

1. _____
2. _____
3. _____

Daily affirmation

_____
_____

Highlights of the Day

1. _____
2. _____
3. _____

What did I learn today?

_____
_____

A single act of kindness throws out roots in all directions,
and the roots spring up and make new trees.
AMELIA EARHART

I am grateful for...

1. _____
2. _____
3. _____

What would make today great?

1. _____
2. _____
3. _____

Daily affirmation

_____
_____

☾

Highlights of the Day

1. _____
2. _____
3. _____

What did I learn today?

_____
_____

Setup screen time on your phone to spend less time on the screen.

I am grateful for...

1. _____
2. _____
3. _____

What would make today great?

1. _____
2. _____
3. _____

Daily affirmation

_____
_____

Highlights of the Day

1. _____
2. _____
3. _____

What did I learn today?

_____
_____

The real voyage of discovery consists not in seeking new lands, but in seeing with new eyes.
MARCEL PROUST

I am grateful for...

1. _____
2. _____
3. _____

What would make today great?

1. _____
2. _____
3. _____

Daily affirmation

_____
_____

Highlights of the Day

1. _____
2. _____
3. _____

What did I learn today?

_____
_____

*Life isn't about getting and having,
it's about giving and being.*
KEVIN KRUSE

I am grateful for...

1. _____
2. _____
3. _____

What would make today great?

1. _____
2. _____
3. _____

Daily affirmation

_____
_____

Highlights of the Day

1. _____
2. _____
3. _____

What did I learn today?

_____
_____

227

Be happy in the moment, that's enough.
Each moment is all we need, not more.
MOTHER TERESA

I am grateful for...

1. _____
2. _____
3. _____

What would make today great?

1. _____
2. _____
3. _____

Daily affirmation

_____
_____

Highlights of the Day

1. _____
2. _____
3. _____

What did I learn today?

_____
_____

The most sincere compliment we can pay is attention.
WALTER ANDERSON

I am grateful for...

1. _____
2. _____
3. _____

What would make today great?

1. _____
2. _____
3. _____

Daily affirmation

_____
_____

Highlights of the Day

1. _____
2. _____
3. _____

What did I learn today?

_____
_____

*Silence is the element in which great things
fashion themselves together.*
THOMAS CARLYLE

I am grateful for...

1. _____
2. _____
3. _____

What would make today great?

1. _____
2. _____
3. _____

Daily affirmation

_____
_____

Highlights of the Day

1. _____
2. _____
3. _____

What did I learn today?

_____
_____

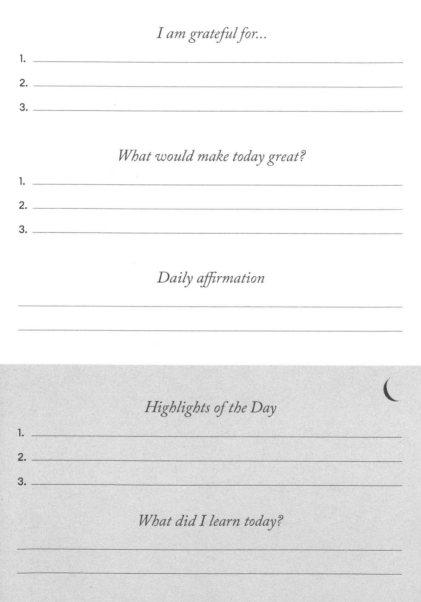

.... / .... / 20 ......

WEEKLY CHALLENGE

*Breathwork can do wonders to your mood and body.
Try box breathing today. Count to four as you follow this order:
inhale, hold, exhale, rest.*

I am grateful for...

1. _____
2. _____
3. _____

What would make today great?

1. _____
2. _____
3. _____

Daily affirmation

_____
_____

Highlights of the Day

1. _____
2. _____
3. _____

What did I learn today?

_____
_____

231

Every morning we get a chance to be different.
A chance to change. A chance to be better.
NICOLE WILLIAMS

I am grateful for...

1. _____
2. _____
3. _____

What would make today great?

1. _____
2. _____
3. _____

Daily affirmation

_____

_____

Highlights of the Day

1. _____
2. _____
3. _____

What did I learn today?

_____

_____

The meaning of life is to find your gift.
The purpose of life is to give it away.
PABLO PICASSO

I am grateful for...

1. _____
2. _____
3. _____

What would make today great?

1. _____
2. _____
3. _____

Daily affirmation

_____
_____

Highlights of the Day

1. _____
2. _____
3. _____

What did I learn today?

_____
_____

Reminder

You have two weeks of the journal left to complete.

We recommend that you order your next
Five Minute Journal from our website:

GET 10% OFF your purchase
CODE: GRATITUDE
intelligentchange.com

We change the world not by what we say or do,
but as a consequence of what we have become.

DR. DAVID HAWKI

I am grateful for...

1. _____
2. _____
3. _____

What would make today great?

1. _____
2. _____
3. _____

Daily affirmation

_____

_____

Highlights of the Day

1. _____
2. _____
3. _____

What did I learn today?

_____

_____

*Everyone of us needs to show how much we care
for each other and, in the process, care for ourselves.*
PRINCESS DIANA

I am grateful for...

1. _____
2. _____
3. _____

What would make today great?

1. _____
2. _____
3. _____

Daily affirmation

_____
_____

Highlights of the Day

1. _____
2. _____
3. _____

What did I learn today?

_____
_____

One word frees us of all the weight and pain of life.
That word is love.

SOPHOCLES

I am grateful for...

1. _____
2. _____
3. _____

What would make today great?

1. _____
2. _____
3. _____

Daily affirmation

_____

_____

Highlights of the Day

1. _____
2. _____
3. _____

What did I learn today?

_____

_____

I've found that there is always some beauty left—
in nature, sunshine, freedom, in yourself;
these can all help you.

ANNE FRANK

I am grateful for...

1. _____
2. _____
3. _____

What would make today great?

1. _____
2. _____
3. _____

Daily affirmation

_____

_____

Highlights of the Day

1. _____
2. _____
3. _____

What did I learn today?

_____

_____

It is not the length of life, but depth of life.
RALPH WALDO EMERSON

I am grateful for...

1. _____
2. _____
3. _____

What would make today great?

1. _____
2. _____
3. _____

Daily affirmation

_____
_____

Highlights of the Day

1. _____
2. _____
3. _____

What did I learn today?

_____
_____

239

Vitality shows not only in the ability to persist but in the ability to start over.

F. SCOTT FITZGERALD

I am grateful for...

1. _____
2. _____
3. _____

What would make today great?

1. _____
2. _____
3. _____

Daily affirmation

_____
_____

Highlights of the Day

1. _____
2. _____
3. _____

What did I learn today?

_____
_____

_ / _ / 20 _

WEEKLY CHALLENGE

This week, plan a feel-good evening with friends.
Invite them over and play board games.

I am grateful for...

1. _____
2. _____
3. _____

What would make today great?

1. _____
2. _____
3. _____

Daily affirmation

_____
_____

Highlights of the Day

1. _____
2. _____
3. _____

What did I learn today?

_____
_____

241

The measure of success is happiness and peace of mind.
BOBBY DAVRO

I am grateful for...

1. _____
2. _____
3. _____

What would make today great?

1. _____
2. _____
3. _____

Daily affirmation

_____
_____

Highlights of the Day

1. _____
2. _____
3. _____

What did I learn today?

_____
_____

If you can't reach your destination by one road, try another.
ELSA SCHIAPARELLI

I am grateful for...

1. _____
2. _____
3. _____

What would make today great?

1. _____
2. _____
3. _____

Daily affirmation

_____
_____

Highlights of the Day

1. _____
2. _____
3. _____

What did I learn today?

_____
_____

Magic is believing in yourself. If you can do that,
you can make anything happen.

JOHANN WOLFGANG VON GOETHE

I am grateful for...

1. _____
2. _____
3. _____

What would make today great?

1. _____
2. _____
3. _____

Daily affirmation

_____
_____

Highlights of the Day

1. _____
2. _____
3. _____

What did I learn today?

_____
_____

☼

It was when I realized I needed to stop trying to be somebody else and be myself, I actually started to own, accept, and love what I had.

TRACEE ELLIS ROSS

I am grateful for...

1. _____
2. _____
3. _____

What would make today great?

1. _____
2. _____
3. _____

Daily affirmation

_____

_____

☾

Highlights of the Day

1. _____
2. _____
3. _____

What did I learn today?

_____

_____

☼

Opening your eyes to more of the world around you
can deeply enhance your gratitude practice.
DERRICK CARPENTER

I am grateful for...

1. _____
2. _____
3. _____

What would make today great?

1. _____
2. _____
3. _____

Daily affirmation

_____
_____

☾

Highlights of the Day

1. _____
2. _____
3. _____

What did I learn today?

_____
_____

I choose to make the rest of my life the best of my life.
LOUISE HAY

I am grateful for...

1. _____
2. _____
3. _____

What would make today great?

1. _____
2. _____
3. _____

Daily affirmation

_____

_____

Highlights of the Day

1. _____
2. _____
3. _____

What did I learn today?

_____

_____

Don't chase people. Be yourself, do your own thing and work hard. The right people—the ones who really belong in your life—will come to you. And stay.

WILL SMITH

I am grateful for...

1. _____
2. _____
3. _____

What would make today great?

1. _____
2. _____
3. _____

Daily affirmation

_____

_____

Highlights of the Day

1. _____
2. _____
3. _____

What did I learn today?

_____

_____

☼

WEEKLY CHALLENGE

*Congratulations! You have just finished six months of the journal.
Take a few minutes to look back through your entries and find
your favorite one. Appreciate what you have written.*

I am grateful for...

1. _____
2. _____
3. _____

What would make today great?

1. _____
2. _____
3. _____

Daily affirmation

_____

_____

☾

Highlights of the Day

1. _____
2. _____
3. _____

What did I learn today?

_____

_____

There's a secret that real writers know that wannabe writers don't, and the secret is this: *It's not the writing part that's hard.* What's hard is sitting down to write. What keeps us from sitting down is *resistance*.

STEVEN PRESSFIELD

Milestones & Coffee Breaks

Congratulations! You have completed 6 months of The Five Minute Journal. Take a few minutes to reflect and reward yourself for creating a wonderful new habit. You have reached for your journal on days when you were already cozy in bed and suddenly remembered you hadn't filled in your entry.

Bravo on beating resistance on both counts.

Now is the time to take a deep breath, smile, and rest a few moments to celebrate this milestone. Milestones exist for us as barometers for how far we have come and also remind us that the journey surely continues. They allow us to take inventory of the past and plan for the future—just like the beginning of the new year, birthdays, and coffee breaks. Please enjoy this milestone by treating yourself to something nice.

HOW HAS THE FIVE MINUTE JOURNAL CHANGED YOUR LIFE?

We'd love to hear your story!
Email us at hello@intelligentchange.com

We also hope you are ready with your new copy of the Journal so you can continue writing tomorrow.

GET 10% OFF your purchase
CODE: GRATITUDE
intelligentchange.com

References

1. 5 Hours and 11 Minutes of TV Per Day
A.C. Nielsen Co (2012)
BLS American Time Use Survey

2. Gratitude
Emmons, R.A. and McCullough, M.E.
(2003) Counting blessings versus burdens:
an experimental investigation of gratitude
and subjective well-being in daily life

3. Hypothalamus
Zahn, R. et al (2008) The Neural Basis
of Human Social Values: Evidence from
Functional MRI

4. Thinking About Watching a Movie
American Physiological Society (April 3,
2006) Just the expectation of a mirthful
laughter experience boosts endorphins 27
percent, HGH, 87 percent.

5. Daily Affirmations
Crum A.J. & Langer, E.J. (2007)
Mindset matters: Exercise and the placebo
effect. Psychological Science, 18(2)

6. The Bad News
http://www.prnewswire.com/
news-releases/dont-be-among-the-
eighty-eight-percent-of-new-years-resolu-
tions-that-fail-1126Five4799.html

NOTES

NOTES

NOTES

NOTES

NOTES

NOTES

NOTES

NOTES

NOTES

NOTES

NOTES